DENVER, COLO

1982

W9-ANM-106

/13

Lieblings~Lieder

unserer Vorväter

American Historical Society of Germans from Russia

Golden Gate Chapter

1982

ISBN #0-914222-06-6

Printer: Hergie & Associates

Typesetter: Corinne Shelton

Preface

In keeping with the purposes of the American Historical Society of Germans from Russia to preserve our unique heritage and to share it with the generations yet to come, the California Golden Gate Chapter has undertaken to prepare a collection of the most beloved songs of our forefathers.

Throughout history, music has played an important part in the daily lives of the German people as they toiled in the fields, as they paused for brief moments of relaxation and as they gathered to worship and sing praises to their God. These were a people who sang in times of joy and sorrow and found in their music a source of faith, encouragement, inspiration, consolation and strength.

We trust that these songs will evoke some special memories of the past as well as kindle a desire to teach them to the future generations and thereby forge a link between our ancestors, ourselves and our posterity.

Music Committee

LaRaine Andereggen
Elaine DeBoer
Arthur Flegel
Cleora Flegel
Frieda Gress
John Gress
Carol Harless
Roswita Niessner
Peggy Scherman

List of Donors

Five Hundred Dollars or more

John & Frieda Gress
Don & Hulda Vowel
Arthur & Cleora Flegel
Robert & Roswita Niessner
Albert & Nell Strohmaier

Two Hundred Dollars or more

Michel & Margaret Rombs
George Bruntz
John & Mary Kindsfather

One Hundred Dollars or more

Robert & Nora Stone
Henry & LaRaine Andereggen
Peggy Scherman
Roy & Eva Kay Warkentin
Peter & Faye Schantz
Catherine Sherry
Lydia Lee Neighbor
Rachel Sullivan
Ruth M. Amen
Rachel Espey
Albert & June Schneider
John & Mary Bolger
Elizabeth Hergert
Alfred & Irene Rader
Margery M. Campanella
Conrad & Wilfriede Hoff
Carol Harless
George & Bernice Reiter
Patricia Yencho
Emil & Ginny Feil
John & Marguerite Siemens

Dedication

This book is dedicated to the memory of our forefathers whose years of labor and loving sacrifice have given us a precious heritage to treasure and to share.

Ein kleines Lied
wie geht's nur an,
daß man so lieb
es haben kann,
was liegt darin?
Erzähle!
Es liegt darin
ein wenig Klang,
ein wenig Wohllaut
und Gesang
und eine ganze
Seele.

Maria Von
Ebner — Eschenbach
1830 — 1916

A simple tune,
How can it be
That it should be
So dear to thee?
What is the reason,
Please explain!
There lies within
A little joy
A little frolic
And a song
And an eternal Soul!

Table of Contents

Gemeinde-Lieder

Allein Gott in der Höh' sei Ehr'

Alone To God In Heaven Be Praise

1. Al - lein Gott in der Höh' sei Ehr' Und Dank für sei - ne Gna - de,
2. Wir lo - ben, preis'n, anbeten dich, Für dei - ne Ehr'; wir dan-ken,

Da-rum, dass nun und nimmermehr Uns rühren kann kein Schade.
Dass du, Gott Va-ter, e-wig - lich, Regiert ohn' al - les Wanken.

Ein Wohl - ge - fall'n Gott an uns hat; Nun ist gross' Fried' ohn'
Ganz un - er - mess'n ist dei - ne Macht, Fort g'schieht, was dein Will'

Un - ter - lass All' Fehd' hat nun ein En - de.
hat be-dacht. Wohl uns des fei - nen Her - ren!

3. O Jesu Christ, Sohn eingebor'n
   Deines himmlischen Vaters,
   Versöhner der, die war'n verlor'n,
   Du Stiller unsers Haders;
   Lamm Gottes, heil' ger Herr und Gott,
   Nimm an die Bitt' von unsrer Not.
   Erbarm' dich unser aller!

4. O heil' ger Geist, du höchstes Gut,
   Du all' rheilsamster Tröster
   Vor's Teufels G'walt fortan behüt'
   Die Jesus Christ erlöset
   Durch grosse Marter und bitter'n Tod!
   Abwend' all unsern Jammer und Not.
   Dazu wir uns verlassen!

1. Alone to God in heaven be praise
   And thanks for all his wondrous deeds,
   For His protection from all harm,
   For His providing of our needs.
   For God so loves us as His own
   Established peace forever more,
   All feud and strife has ended.

2. We praise, adore and honor you
   And thank you God, our gracious king,
   For you, our Father, without fail
   Eternally are reigning.
   Your power is great, mighty your deed,
   All will be done as you decreed,
   There is none other equal.

1

Die Ehre Gottes aus der Natur

The Heavens Are Declaring

1. The heav'ns are declaring the Lord's endless glory,
   Thro' all the earth His praise is found.
   The seas re-echo the marvellous story.
   O man, repeat that glorious sound.
   The starry host He orders and measures,
   He fills the morning's golden springs;
   He wakes the sun from his night curtained slumbers,
   Oh, man adore the King of Kings;
   Oh man, adore the King of Kings.

2. What power and splendor, and wisdom and order,
   In nature's mighty plan unroll'd!
   Thro' space and time to infinity's border.
   What wonders vast and manifold.
   The earth is His, and the heav'ns o'er it bending
   The Maker in His works behold!
   He is, and will be, Thro' ages unending,
   A God of strength and love untold,
   A God of strength and love untold.

Ach bleib mit deiner Gnade

Oh Keep Your Loving Graces

1. Ach bleib' mit dei-ner Gna-de Bei uns Herr Je-su Christ,

Dass uns hin-fort nicht scha-de Des bö-sen Fein-des List!

2. Ach bleib' mit deinem Worte
   Bei uns, Erlöser wert,
   Dass uns sei hier und dorte
   Viel Gut' und Heil beschert!

3. Ach bleib' mit deinem Segen
   Bei uns, du reicher Herr!
   Dein' Gnad' und Heilsvermögen
   Reichlich in uns vermehr'!

4. Ach bleib' mit deiner Treue
   Bei uns, du Herr und Gott!
   Bestandigkeit verleihe,
   Hilf uns aus aller Not.

1. Oh keep your loving Graces
   With us dear Christ above
   That there will be no falling
   But keep us in your love.

2. Thy word may always bless us
   With us forever more
   Stay near and keep us trusting
   That we will all adore.

3. Oh, stay with thine own blessings
   With us, you truthful peer
   Your Grace and sin forgiving
   With riches, luck and cheer.

4. Oh, stay with thine own power
   With us, dear Lord and God
   Trust worthiness our bower
   With help in all our need.

3

Befiehl du deine Wege

All Glory, Laud and Honor

1. Be - fiehl du dei-ne We - ge Und was dein Her-ze kränkt,
   Der al - ler - treu-sten Pflege Des, der den Himmel lenkt!

Der Wol-ken, Luft und Win - den Gibt We-ge, Lauf und Bahn,

Der wird auch We-ge fin - den, Da dein Fuss ge-hen kann.

2. Dem Herrn musst du vertrauen,
   Wenn dir's soll wohl ergeh'n;
   Auf sein Werk musst du schauen,
   Wenn dein Werk soll besteh'n.
   Mit Sorgen und mit Grämen
   Und selbstgemachter Pein
   Lässt Gott sich gar nichts nehmen,
   Er muss erbeten sein.

3. Dein' ew'ge Treu' und Gnade,
   O Vater, sieh es recht,
   Was gut sei oder schade
   Dem sterblichen Geschlecht;
   Und was du dann erlesen,
   Das treibst du, starker Held,
   Und bringst zu Stand und Wesen,
   Was deinem Rat gefällt.

1. All glory, laud, and honor
   To Thee, Redeemer, King,
   To whom the lips of children
   Made sweet hosannas ring!
   The people of the Hebrews
   With palms before Thee went;
   Our praise and prayer and anthems
   Before Thee we present.

2. Thou art the King of Israel,
   Thou David's royal Son,
   Who in the Lord's name comest,
   The King and blessed One!
   To Thee, before Thy Passion,
   They sang their hymns of praise;
   To Thee, now high exalted,
   Our melody we raise.

3. Thou didst accept their praises;
   Accept the prayers we bring,
   Who in all good delightest,
   Thou good and gracious King!
   All glory, laud, and honor
   To Thee, Redeemer, King,
   To whom the lips of children
   Made sweet hosannas ring!

4

Es ist das Heil uns kommen her

The Savior Now Has Come To Us

1. Es ist das Heil uns kommen her Voll Gnad' und lauter Gü-te;
Die Wer-ke ge-ben nimmermehr Den Frie-den ins Ge-mü-te.
Der Glaub' sieht Je-sum Chri-stum an, Der hat ge-nug für uns ge-tan, Er ist der Mitt-ler wor-den.

2. Sei Lob und Ehr' mit hohem Preis
Um dieser Wohltat willen
Gott Vater, Sohn und heil'gem Geist;
Der woll' mit Gnad' erfüllen,
Was er in uns begonnen hat
Zu Ehren seiner Macht und Gnad',
Dass heilig werd' sein Name!

3. Gerecht vor Gott sind die allein,
Die dieses Glaubens leben;
Dann wird des Glaubens heller Schein
Durch Werke kund sich geben.
Der Glaub' ist wohl mit Gott daran,
Und aus der Nächstenlieb' sieht man,
Dass du aus Gott geboren.

1. The Saviour now has come to us
In grace and loving kindness
Works can no longer peace provide
Our spirit's need for goodness.
For Jesus sees our faith alone
So much for us he now has done
He is our Intercessor.

2. High praise and honor of great price
For this great blessing bringing;
God, Father, Son and Holy Ghost
His grace thereby fulfilling
What he has chosen to begin,
Love, honor, praise, without, within,
Is due His holy presence.

3. Righteous to God are those alone
Who in His faith are living.
In loving care our faith is shown
By works that have true meaning.
Faith shows itself within God's plan
As care we give our fellow man
For this God sent His Saviour.

5

Ein' feste Burg

A Mighty Fortress Is Our God

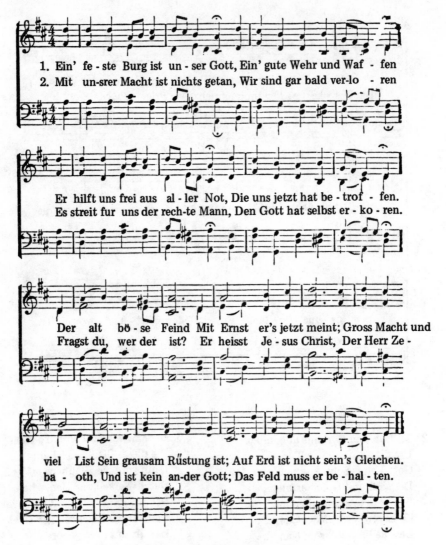

1. Ein' fe - ste Burg ist un - ser Gott, Ein' gute Wehr und Waf - fen

2. Mit un-srer Macht ist nichts getan, Wir sind gar bald ver-lo - ren

Er hilft uns frei aus al - ler Not, Die uns jetzt hat be - trof - fen.

Es streit fur uns der rech-te Mann, Den Gott hat selbst er - ko - ren.

Der alt bö - se Feind Mit Ernst er's jetzt meint; Gross Macht und

Fragst du, wer der ist? Er heisst Je - sus Christ, Der Herr Ze -

viel List Sein grausam Rüstung ist; Auf Erd ist nicht sein's Gleichen.

ba - oth, Und ist kein an-der Gott; Das Feld muss er be - hal - ten.

3. Und wenn die Welt voll Teufel wär'
Und wollt' uns gar verschlingen,
So fürchten wir uns nicht so sehr;
Es soll uns doch gelingen.
Der Fürst dieser Welt,
Wie sau'r er sich stellt,
Tut er uns doch nichts;
Das macht, er ist gericht't,
Ein Wörtlein kann ihn fällen.

4. Das Wort sie sollen lassen stah'n
Und kein Dank dazu haben.
Er ist bei uns wohl auf dem Plan
Mit seinem Geist und Gaben.
Nehmen sie den Leib.
Gut, Ehr, Kind und Weib
Lass fahren dahin,
Sie haben's kein Gewinn;
Das Reich muss uns doch bleiben.

1. A mighty fortress is our God, A bulwark never failing;
   Our helper He, amid the flood Of mortal ills prevailing,
   For still our ancient foe Doth seek to work us woe;
   His craft and pow'r are great, And, armed with cruel hate,
   On earth is not his equal.

2. Did we in our own strength confide, Our striving would be losing;
   Were not the right Man on our side, The Man of God's own choosing.
   Dost ask who that may be? Christ Jesus, it is He;
   Lord Sabaoth is His name, From age to age the same,
   And He must win the battle.

3. And tho' this world, with devils filled, Should threaten to undo us;
   We will not fear, for God hath willed His truth to triumph through us.
   The prince of darkness grim — We tremble not for him;
   His rage we can endure, For lo! his doom is sure,
   One little word shall fell him.

4. That word above all earthly pow'rs — No thanks to them — abideth:
   The Spirit and the gifts are ours Thro' Him who with us sideth.
   Let goods and kindred go, This mortal life also;
   The body they may kill: God's truth abideth still,
   His kingdom is forever.

Zum Anfang des Gottesdienstes

Herr, öffne mir die Herzenstür, zeuch mein Herz durch dein
Wort zu dir, lass mich dein Wort bewahren rein, lass mich dein Kind
und Erbe sein.

Ehre sei dem Vater und dem Sohne und dem heiligen Geiste, wie
es war im Anfang, jetzt und immerdar sein wird, in alle Ewigkeit.
Amen.

Das Gebet des Herrn

Unser Vater, der du bist im Himmel, Dein Name werde
geheiliget. Dein Reich komme. Dein Wille geschehe auf Erden
wie im Himmel. Unser täglich Brot gib uns heute. Vergib uns
unsre Schuld, wie wir vergeben unsern Schuldigern. Und
führe uns nicht in Versuchung, sondern erlöse uns von dem
Uebel. Denn dein ist das Reich, und die Kraft, und die Herrlichkeit
in Ewigkeit. Amen.

Gott ist gegenwärtig

God Is Here Among Us

Gott ist gegen-wär - tig. Las-set uns an - be - ten und in Ehrfurcht vor ihn tre - ten!
Gott ist in der Mit - te. Al-les in uns schwei-ge und sich in-nigst vor ihm beu - ge!

Wer ihn kennt, wer ihn nennt, schlag'die Au-gen nie - der; gebt das Herz ihm wie - der!

2. Gott is gegenwärtig,
   Dem die Cherubinen
   Tag und Nacht mit Ehrfurcht dienen:
   Heilig, heilig, heilig
   Singen ihm zur Ehre
   Aller Engel hohe Chöre.
   Herr, vernimm
   Unsre Stimm',
   Wenn auch wir Geringen
   Unsre Opfer bringen.

3. Mache mich einfältig,
   Innig, abgeschieden,
   Sanft und still in deinem Frieden!
   Mach' mich reines Herzens,
   Dass ich deine Klarheit
   Schau' im Geist und in der Wahrheit!
   Lass mein Herz
   Überwärts
   Wie ein Adler schweben
   Und in dir nur leben!

1. God is here among us
   Let us now adore Him
   And in praise bow down before Him.
   God is in His temple
   Calls us all to silence
   Inwardly to feel His presence.
   Him to know, our love to show,
   As in full surrender
   We, our hearts now tender.

2. God is here among us,
   Him the cherubs honor
   Night and day to seek his favor.
   Holy, holy, holy,
   Angel chorus swelling
   Sing His praises e'er rejoicing.
   Hear our plea, Lord we pray
   As your humble beings
   Now their gifts are bringing.

3. Make of me your servant
   In this quiet moment
   May your peace imbue my spirit.
   Purify my heart, Lord
   As I hear your message
   Let me feel within your presence.
   Lead my soul to new heights
   As an eagle soaring,
   Evermore adoring.

Grosser Gott, wir loben dich

Holy God, We Praise Thy Name

1. Grosser Gott, wir lo - ben Dich! Herr, wir preisen Dei - ne Stärke!
2. Auf dem gan - zen Er - den-kreis Loben Grosse Dich und Kleine.
3. Sie verehrt du heil'ger Geist, Welcher uns mit Sei - nen Lehren
4. Ste - he denn, o Herr, uns bei, Die wir Dich in De - mut bitten:

Vor Dir neigt die Er - de sich Und be - wun - dert Deine Werke.
Dir, Gott Va - ter, Dir zum Preis Singt die hei - li - ge Ge - mei - ne,
Und mit Trost gar kräftig speist, Dich, den Herrscher voller Ehren
Sprich von al - ler Schuld uns frei, Da Du auch für uns gelitten;

Wie Du warst vor al - ler Zeit, So bleibst Du in Ewigkeit!
Und verehrt auf Seinem Thron Deinen eingebornen Sohn.
Der mit Dir, o Je - su Christ, Und dem Va - ter Eines ist!
Nimm uns nach vollbrachtem Lauf Zu Dir in den Himmel auf!   A - men.

1. Holy God, we praise Thy name;
   Lord of all, we bow before Thee;
   All on earth Thy scepter claim,
   All in heav'n above adore Thee.
   Infinite Thy vast domain,
   Everlasting is Thy reign.

2. Hark, the loud celestial hymn,
   Angel choirs above are raising;
   Cherubim and Seraphim,
   In unceasing chorus praising,
   Fill the heav'ns with sweet accord:
   Holy, holy, holy Lord.

3. Lo! the apostolic train,
   Joins Thy sacred name to hallow;
   Prophets swell the glad refrain,
   And the white-robed martyrs follow;
   And, from morn to set of sun,
   Through the Church the song goes on.

4. Holy Father, Holy Son,
   Holy Spirit, Three we name Thee;
   While in essence only One,
   Undivided God we claim Thee,
   And adoring bend the knee,
   While we sing our praise to Thee.

9

Heilig, heilig, heilig

Holy, Holy, Holy!

1. Hei - lig, hei - lig, hei - lig! Gott, E - wig - Va - ter!
2. Hei - lig, hei - lig, hei - lig! Hei - li - ge an - be - ten!
3. Hei - lig, hei - lig, hei - lig! Ob dich Nacht verhül - let,
4. Hei - lig, hei - lig, hei - lig! Gott, E - wig - Va - ter!

Hör' wie dei - ner Kin - der Lied dich Ew'gen stau - nend preist.
Vor dir legt die Kronen hin der Ü - ber - win - der Schar.
Ob auch sün - dig Menschenaug' nicht schaut die Herrlich - keit,
Dei - ner Schöpfung Wunderpracht, Herr, deinen Na - men preist;

Hei - lig, hei - lig, hei - lig! Gnä - dig und all - mäch - tig!
Che - ru - bim und Sera - phim prei - send vor dich tre - ten,
Du al - lein bist hei - lig, der die Welt er - fül - let,
Hei - lig, hei - lig, hei - lig! Gnä - dig und all - mäch - tig!

Herr, Gott Je - ho - vah, Va - ter, Sohn und Geist.
Der war und ist und sein wird im - mer - dar.
Glor-reich in Lie - be, Kraft und Hei - lig - keit.
Herr, Gott Je - ho - vah, Va - ter, Sohn und Geist. A - men.

1. Holy, holy, holy! Lord God Almighty!
   Early in the morning our song shall rise to Thee;
   Holy, holy, holy, merciful and mighty!
   God in Three Persons, blessed Trinity!

2. Holy, holy holy! All the saints adore Thee,
   Casting down their golden crowns around the glassy sea;
   Cherubim and seraphim falling down before Thee,
   Which wert and art and evermore shalt be.

3. Holy, holy, holy! Tho' the darkness hide Thee,
   Tho' the eye of sinful man Thy glory may not see,
   Only Thou art holy; there is none beside Thee,
   Perfect in pow'r, in love, and purity.

4. Holy, holy, holy! Lord God almighty!
   All Thy works shall praise Thy name in earth and sky and sea.
   Holy, holy holy, merciful and mighty!
   God in Three Persons, blessed Trinity!

Herr Jesu Christ, dich zu uns wend'

Lord Jesus, Now To Thee We Wend

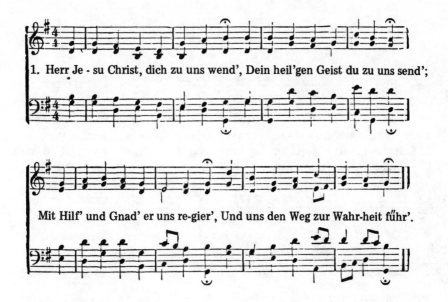

1. Herr Je - su Christ, dich zu uns wend', Dein heil'gen Geist du zu uns send';

Mit Hilf' und Gnad' er uns re-gier', Und uns den Weg zur Wahr-heit führ'.

2. Tu' auf den Mund zum Lobe dein,
   Bereit' das Herz zur Andacht fein;
   Den Glauben mehr', stärk' den Verstand,
   Dass uns dein Nam' werd' wohl bekannt.

3. Ehr' sei dem Vater und dem Sohn,
   Dem heil'gen Geist in einem Thron!
   Der heiligen Dreifaltigkeit
   Sei Lob und Preis in Ewigkeit.

1. Lord Jesus, now to Thee we wend;
   Your Holy Spirit to us send.
   Your love and grace shall be our guide,
   As we in truth with you abide.

2. Open our mouths to sing your praise.
   Prepare our hearts to seek your ways.
   Strengthen our faith, imbue our minds
   To bless your name for all mankind.

3. Praise to the Father and the Son
   And Holy Ghost, all on one throne.
   The holy, blessed Trinity
   Praise now and for eternity.

A Call To Worship

Oh come, let us sing unto the Lord;
Let us make a joyful noise to the rock
of our salvation.

Let us come before His presence with
thanksgiving; and make a joyful noise
unto Him with psalms.

Oh come, let us worship and bow down;
Let us kneel before the Lord, our Maker:
For He is our God,
And we are the people of His pasture,
and the sheep of His hand.

11

Jesu geh' voran

Jesus Still Lead On

1. Je - su, geh' vor - an, Auf der Le - bens - bahn, Und, wir
2. Soll's uns hart ergeh'n, Lass uns fes - te stehn, Und auch
3. Ordne un - sern Gang, Je - su le - bens - lang; Führst du

wol -len nicht ver - wei - len, Dir ge - treu - lich, nach - zu - ei -
in den schwersten Ta - gen, Nie - mals ü - ber Las - ten kla -
uns durch rauhe We - ge, Gib uns auch die nöt - ge Pfle -

len; Führ uns an der Hand Bis ins Va - ter - land!
gen; Denn durch Trübsal hier Geht der Weg zu dir!
ge; Tu' uns nach dem Lauf Dei - ne Tü - re auf!

A - men.

1. Jesus lead the way
   Through our life's long day
   And with faithful footstep steady
   We will follow, ever ready.
   Guide us by Thy hand
   To the Fatherland.

2. Should our lot be hard,
   Keep us on our guard;
   Even through severest trial,
   Make us brave in self denial;
   Transient pain may be
   But a way to Thee.

3. Order Thou our ways,
   Saviour, all our days,
   If Thou lead us through rough places,
   Grant us Thy sustaining graces
   When our course is o'er,
   Open heavens door.

Jesu meines Lebens Leben

Christ The Life Of All The Living

Je-su meines Lebens Leben, Je-su, meines To-des Tod,

1. Der du dich für mich ge-ge-ben In die tief-ste See--len-not,

In das äu-sser-ste Ver-der-ben, Nur dass ich nicht möchte sterben.

Tau-send-, tausendmal sei dir, Liebster Je-su, Dank da-für!

2. Du, ach du hast ausgestanden
   Lästerreden, Spott und Hohn,
   Und du gingst in schweren Banden,
   Du gerechter Gottes Sohn,
   Nur mich Armen zu erretten
   Von den argen Sündenketten,
   Tausend-, tausendmal sei dir,
   Liebster Jesu, Dank dafür!

3. Nun, ich danke dir von Herzen,
   Herr, für alle deine Not
   Für die Wunden, für die Schmerzen,
   Für den herben, bittern Tod;
   Für dein Zittern, für dein Zagen,
   Für die tausendfachen Plagen
   Für die Angst und tiefe Pein
   Will ich ewig dankbar sein!

1. Christ, the Life of all the living,
   Christ, the Death of death, our foe,
   Who, Thyself for me once giving
   To the darkest depths of woe,—
   Thro' Thy suff'rings, death, and merit
   I eternal life inherit:
   Thousand, thousand thanks shall be,
   Dearest Jesus, unto Thee.

2. Thou, ah! Thou, hast taken on Thee
   Bonds and stripes, a cruel rod;
   Pain and scorn were heaped upon Thee,
   O Thou sinless Son of God!
   Thus didst Thou my soul deliver
   From the bonds of sin forever.
   Thousand, thousand thanks shall be,
   Dearest Jesus, unto Thee.

3. Then, for all that wrought my pardon,
   For Thy sorrows deep and dire,
   For Thine anguish in the Garden,
   I will thank Thee evermore,
   Thank Thee for Thy groaning, sighing,
   For Thy bleeding and Thy dying,
   For that last triumphant cry,
   And shall praise Thee, Lord, on high.

13

Jesus, meine Zuversicht

Jesus, Living Savior Mine

Je-sus, mei - ne Zu - ver - sicht und mein Hei-land, ist im Le - - ben!
Die-ses weiß ich; sollt' ich nicht dar - um mich zu - frie-den ge - - ben,

was die lan - ge To - des - nacht mir auch für Ge - dan-ken macht?

1. Jesus, living Savior mine,
   My assurance all exceeding
   This I know, therefore I will
   Be content and trust his leading.
   Even through the night of death
   He's my hope till my last breath.

Unsern Ausgang segne Gott

1. Unsern Ausgang segne Gott, Unsern Eingang gleicher - ma - ssen,
   Segne un-ser täglich Brot, Segne unser Tun und Las - sen;

Segne uns mit selgem Sterben Und mach' uns zu Himmelserben.

Lobe den Herren, o meine Seele

Praise Ye the Lord, Oh My Soul

1. Lo-be den Her-ren, o mei-ne See-le! Ich will ihn lo-ben bis in Tod;
   weil ich noch Stunden auf Er-den zäh-le, will ich lob-sin-gen mei-nem Gott.
2. Se-lig, ja se-lig ist der zu nen-nen, des Hil-fe der Gott Ja-kobs ist;
   wel-cher vom Glauben sich nicht läßt tren-nen und hofft ge-trost auf Je-sum Christ.
3. Rühmet ihr Menschen, den ho-hen Na-men des, der so gro-ße Wun-der tut!
   Al-les was O-dem hat, ru-fe A-men und brin-ge Lob mit fro-hem Mut!

1. Der Leib und Seel' ge-ge-ben hat, wer-de ge-prie-sen
2. Wer die-sen Herrn zum Bei-stand hat, fin-det am be-sten
3. Ihr Kin-der Got-tes, lobt und preist Va-ter und Sohn und

früh und spat.
Rat und Tat.   } Hal-le-lu-ja, hal-le-lu-ja!
heil'-gen Geist!

---

1. Praise ye the Lord, Oh my soul, praise His name
   Praise Him forever until my death.
   While a sojourner on earth I remain,
   I will sing praises with all my breath
   To God who body and soul us bore
   Glory and praise forever more.
   Hallelujah!

2. Blessed, eternally blessed is He
   Whose help is God in his heavenly throne,
   He who unswervingly faithful will be
   Whose hope is Jesus Christ alone.
   He who confesses him as Lord
   Finds help and guidance in His word.
   Hallelujah!

3. Praise ye all people the holy name
   Of Him who wondrous things has wrought
   Those who have breath in them shout ye "Amen"
   With cheerful hearts bring praise and laud!
   Exalt His honor, praise Him most,
   Father and Son and Holy Ghost.
   Hallelujah!

15

Näher, mein Gott zu dir

Nearer My God to Thee

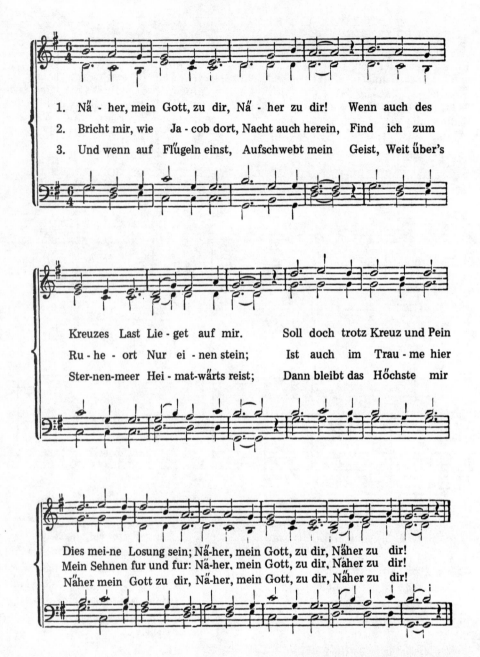

1. Nä - her, mein Gott, zu dir, Nä - her zu dir! Wenn auch des
2. Bricht mir, wie Ja - cob dort, Nacht auch herein, Find ich zum
3. Und wenn auf Flügeln einst, Aufschwebt mein Geist, Weit über's

Kreuzes Last Lie - get auf mir. Soll doch trotz Kreuz und Pein
Ru - he - ort Nur ei - nen stein; Ist auch im Trau - me hier
Ster-nen-meer Hei - mat-wärts reist; Dann bleibt das Höchste mir

Dies mei-ne Losung sein; Nä-her, mein Gott, zu dir, Näher zu dir!
Mein Sehnen fur und fur: Nä-her, mein Gott, zu dir, Näher zu dir!
Näher mein Gott zu dir, Nä-her, mein Gott, zu dir, Näher zu dir!

1. Nearer my God, to Thee, Nearer to Thee;
   E'en though it be a cross that raiseth me.
   Still all my song shall be — Nearer my God to Thee,
   Nearer my God to Thee; Nearer to Thee!

2. Tho' like the wanderer, the sun gone down
   Darkness be over me, My rest a stone.
   Yet in my dreams I'd be nearer my God to Thee,
   Nearer my God to Thee; Nearer to Thee!

3. Or, if on joyful wings, Cleaving the sky,
   Sun, moon and stars forgot, Upward I fly,
   Still all my song shall be — Nearer my God to Three,
   Nearer my God to Thee, nearer to Thee!

O Welt sieh hier dein Leben

Upon the Cross Extended

1. O Welt! sieh hier dein Le - ben Am Stamm des Kreu-zes schwe-ben,

Dein Heil sinkt in den Tod! Der grosse Fürst der Eh - ren Lässt

wil-lig sich be - schweren Mit Schlä-gen, Hohn und grossem Spott.

2. Wer hat Dich so geschlagen,
Mein Heil! und Dich mit Plagen
So ubel zugericht't?
Du bist ja nicht ein Sünder,
Wie wir und unsre Kinder,
Von Missetaten weisst Du nicht.

3. Ich, ich und meine Sünden,
Die sich wie Körnlein finden
Des Sandes an dem Meer,
Die haben Dir erreget
Das Elend, das Dich schläget,
Das grosse, starke Marterheer.

1. Upon the cross extended,
See, world, thy Lord suspended,
Thy Saviour yields His breath.
The Prince of Life from heaven
Himself hath freely given
To shame and blows and bitter death.

2. Come hither now and ponder,
'Twill fill thy soul with wonder,
Blood streams from every pore.
Through grief whose depth none knoweth,
From His great heart there floweth
Sign after sign of anguish o'er.

3. How God at our transgression
To anger gives expression,
How loud His thunders roll,
How fearfully He smiteth,
How sorely He requiteth,—
All this Thy sufferings teach my soul.

17

Tochter Zion, Freue dich

Daughter of Zion

1. Toch - ter Zi - on, freu - e dich, jauch - ze laut, Je - ru - sa lem! Sieh, dein Kö - nig kommt zu dir! Ja, er kommt, der Frie - de - fürst! Toch - ter Zi - on, freu - e dich, jauch - ze laut, Je - ru - sa - lem!

2. Ho - si - an - na, Da - vids Sohn, sei ge - seg - net dei - nem Volk! Grün - de nun dein ew' - ges Reich, Ho - si - an - na in der Höh'! Ho - si - an - na, Da - vids Sohn, sei ge - seg - net dei - nem Volk!

3. Ho - si - an - na, Da - vids Sohn, sei ge - grü - sset, Kö - nig mild! E - wig steht dein Frie - dens - thron, du, des ew' - gen Va - ters Kind! Ho - si - an - na, Da - vids Sohn, sei ge - grü - sset, Kö - nig mild!

Daughter of Zion greatly rejoice,
Shout with joy, Jerusalem!
Oh, behold, your King has come to you!
Oh, behold, the Prince of Peace!
Daughter of Zion greatly rejoice,
Shout with joy, Jerusalem.

Tut mir auf die schőne Pforte

Open Now The Gates Of Beauty

1. Tut mir auf die schő-ne Pfor-te, Fűhrt in Got-tes Haus mich ein!
   Ach wie wird an die-sem Or - te Mei - ne See - le frő - lich sein!

Hier ist Got - tes An - ge - sicht, Hier ist lau - ter Trost und Licht.

2. Herr, ich bin zu dir gekommen,
   Komme du nun auch zu mir!
   Wo du Wohnung hast genommen,
   Da ist lauter Himmel hier.
   Zieh' du in mein Herz hinein,
   Lass es deinen Tempel sein!

3. Du, o Herr, gibst Kraft den Deinen
   Und den Schwachen allermeist;
   Darum gib mir deinen reinen,
   Deinen guten, stillen Geist,
   Dass, es gelte wo und wann,
   Ich dir stille halten kann!

1. Open now the gates of beauty
   For God's house to enter in
   At this place I feel His presence
   And joy fills my soul within.
   Heavenly beauty fills this place
   Here is ever light and grace.

2. Gracious God, I come before Thee
   Come Thou also down to me.
   Where we find Thee and adore Thee,
   There a heaven on earth must be.
   To my heart, oh enter Thou,
   Let it be Thy temple now.

3. Grant, oh Lord, strength to the weary
   And protect those who are Thine
   Though my toilsome paths be dreary
   Let your spirit in me shine.
   For whate'er my lot shall be
   I will surely follow Thee.

Was Gott tut, das ist wohl getan

What God Does That Is So Well Done

Was Gott tut, das ist wohl ge-tan. Es bleibt ge-recht sein Wil - le.
Wie er fängt mei-ne Sa-chen an, will ich ihm hal - ten stil - le.
Er ist mein Gott, der

in der Not mich wohl weiss zu er - hal - ten; drum lass ich ihn nur wal - ten.

2. Was Gott tut, das ist wohlgetan;
   Er wird mich nicht betrügen.
   Er fuhret mich auf rechter Bahn:
   So lass ich mir genügen
   An seiner Huld
   Und hab' Geduld;
   Er wird mein Unglück wenden,
   Es steht in seinen Händen.

3. Was Gott tut, das ist wohlgetan:
   Dabei will ich verbleiben.
   Es mag mich auf die rauhe Bahn
   Not, Tod und Elend treiben,
   So wird Gott mich
   Ganz väterlich
   In seinen Armen halten:
   Drum lass ich ihn nur walten.

1. What God does that is so well done
   His righteous will is present
   As all my doings He directs.
   I will in turn be rev'rent.
   He is my God who knows my needs.
   He is my sure deliverer
   And He shall be my ruler.

2. What God does that is so well done
   He saves me from perdition.
   He guides me in His righteous ways
   For me a blest condition.
   I trust His grace, wait patiently
   He'll guard me from affliction
   His hands control my mission.

3. What God does that is so well done
   In this I am abiding
   Though driven by life's rueful way
   Of death, of pain and misery.
   For God will still, most fatherly
   In His warm arms enfold me.
   For this he came to save me.

20

Wer nur den lieben Gott lässt walten

If Thou But Suffer God to Guide Thee

Wer nur den lie-ben Gott läßt wal-ten und hof-fet auf ihn al-le-zeit,
den wird er wun-der-bar er-hal-ten in al-ler Not und Trau-rig-keit.

Wer Gott, dem Al-ler-höch-sten, traut, der hat auf kei-nen Sand ge-baut.

2. Was helfen uns die schweren Sorgen?
Was hilft uns unser Weh und Ach?
Was hilft es, dass wir alle Morgen
Beseufzen unser Ungemach?
Wir machen unser Kreuz und Leid
Nur grösser durch die Traurigkeit.

3. Drum halte nur ein wenig stille
Und warte in dir selbst vergnügt,
Wie unsers Gottes Gnadenwille
Und sein allweiser Rat es fügt!
Gott, der uns ihm hat auserwählt,
Der weiss am besten, was uns fehlt.

4. Er kennt die rechten Freudenstunden,
Er weiss wohl, was uns nützlich sei;
Wenn er uns nur hat treu erfunden
Und merket keine Heuchelei,
So kommt er, eh' wir's uns verseh'n
Und lässet uns viel Gut's gescheh'n.

1. If thou but suffer God to guide thee
And hope in Him thro' all thy ways,
He'll give thee strength, whate'er betide thee
And bear thee thro' the evil days.
Who trust in God's unchanging love
Builds on the Rock that naught can move.

2. What can these anxious cares avail thee,
These never ceasing moans and sighs?
What can it help if thou bewail thee
O'er each dark moment as it flies?
Our cross and trials do but press
The heavier for our bitterness.

3. Be patient and await His leisure
In cheerful hope, with heart content
To take whate'er thy Father's pleasure
And His discerning love hath sent,
Nor doubts our inmost wants are known
To Him who chose us for His own.

4. God knows full well when times of gladness
Shall be the needful thing for thee,
When He has tried thy soul with sadness
And from all guile has found thee free,
He comes to thee all unaware
And makes thee own His loving care.

Wie soll ich dich empfangen

O Lord How Shall I Meet Thee

Wie soll ich dich emp - fan - gen Und wie be-gegn' ich dir,
O al - ler Welt Ver - lan - gen, O mei-ner See - le Zier?

O Je-su, Je-su, set - ze Dein gött-lich Licht mir bei,

Da - mit, was dich er-göt - ze, Mir kund und wissend sei.

2. Ich lag in schweren Banden,
   Du kommst und machst mich los;
   Ich stand in Spott und Schanden,
   Du kommst und machst mich gross,
   Und hebst mich hoch zu Ehren
   Und schenkst mir grosses Gut,
   Das sich nicht lässt verzehren,
   Wie Erdenreichtum tut.

3. Er kommt zum Weltgerichte,
   Zum Fluch dem, der ihm flucht;
   Mit Gnad' und süssem Lichte
   Dem, der ihn liebt und sucht.
   Ach komm', ach komm', o Sonne,
   Und hol' uns allzumal
   Zum ew'gen Licht, zur Wonne
   Zu deinem Freudensaal!

1. O Lord, how shall I meet Thee,
   How welcome Thee aright?
   Thy people long to greet Thee,
   My Hope, my heart's Delight!
   Oh, kindle, Lord, most holy,
   Thy lamp within my breast
   To do in spirit lowly
   All that may please Thee best.

2. I lay in fetters, groaning,
   Thou com'st to set me free;
   I stood, my shame bemoaning,
   Thou com'st to honor me;
   A glory Thou dost give me,
   A treasure safe on high,
   That will not fail or leave me
   As earthly riches fly.

3. He comes to judge the nations,
   A terror to His foes,
   A Light of consolations
   And Blessed Hope to those
   Who love the Lord's appearing
   O glorious Sun, now come
   Send forth Thy beams most cheering,
   And guide us safely home.

22

Auf, denn die Nacht wird kommen

Work, For The Night Is Coming

1. Auf, denn die Nacht wird kom-men, Auf mit dem jun-gen Tag;
2. Auf, denn die Nacht wird kom-men, Auf, wenn es Mit-tag ist
3. Auf, denn die Nacht wird kom-men, Auf, wenn die Son-ne weicht,

Wir - ket am frü - hen Mor - gen, Eh's zu spät sein mag!
Wei - het die be - sten Kräf - te Dem Herrn Je - su Christ!
Auf, wenn der Ab-end na - het Wenn der Tag ent fleucht!

Wir - ket im Licht der Son - nen, Fan - get bei zei - ten an;
Wir - ket mit Ernst, ihr From-men, Gebt al - les an - dre dran;
Auf, bis zum letz-ten Zu - ge, Wen - det nur Fleiss dar - an;

Chorus:

Auf, denn die Nacht wird kom-men, Da man nicht mehr kann!

1. Work, for the night is coming, Work thro' the morning hours;
Work while the dew is sparkling, Work 'mid springing flow'rs;
Work, when the day grows brighter, Work in the glowing sun;
Work, for the night is coming, When man's work is done.

2. Work for the night is coming, Work through the sunny noon;
Fill brightest hours with labor, Rest comes sure and soon,
Give every flying minute, something to keep in store;
Work for the night is coming, When man works no more.

3. Work, for the night is coming, Under the sunset skies;
While their brights tints are glowing, Work for daylight flies,
Work till the last beam fadeth, Fadeth to shine no more;
Work, while the night is darkening, When man's work is o'er.

Bringen Garben ein

Bringing In The Sheaves

1. Die mit Tränen sä - en, ern-ten einst mit Freuden! Herrlich wird der
2. Sä - et denn am Morgen ed-len Lie - bes - sa - men, Hal-tet auch am
3. Sä - end für den Heiland wo er uns hin - sen - det, Sa-men und Ver-

Ju - bel ein-stens droben sein. Gu-ten Sa-men streu-en, die der
Mit-tag eu - re Hand nicht ein, Sä - et bis am A - bend dunkle
mö-gen will er uns ver-leih'n Er ver-heisst den Se-gen und wir

Herr ge-sen-det, Und sie wer-den freu-dig Gar-ben brin-gen ein.
Schatten ziehen, Herrlich wird die Ernt für euch am En - de sein.
war - ten freudig, Bringen ihm zu Eh - ren uns'-re Gar-ben ein.

Chorus

Gar-ben brin-gen ein, Gar-ben brin-gen ein! Die mit Tränen

sä - en, brin-gen Gar-ben ein! Brin-gen Gar-ben ein! Brin-gen

Gar - ben ein! Ernten einst mit Freuden! Brin-gen Gar-ben ein!

1. Sowing in the morning, sowing seeds of kindness
   Sowing in the noontide and the dewy eve.
   Waiting for the harvest and the time of reaping;
   We shall come rejoicing, bringing in the sheaves.

Chorus:
   Bringing in the sheaves, bringing in the sheaves,
   We shall come rejoicing bringing in the sheaves,
   Bringing in the sheaves, bringing in the sheaves,
   We shall come rejoicing, bringing in the sheaves.

2. Sowing in the sunshine, sowing in the shadows,
   Fearing neither clouds nor winter's chilling breeze;
   By and by the harvest and the labor ended;
   We shall come rejoicing, bringing in the sheaves.

3. Going forth in weeping, sowing for the Master,
   Tho' the loss sustain'd our spirit often grieves;
   When our weeping's over, He will bid us welcome;
   We shall come rejoicing, bringing in the sheaves.

Sanctus

Holy, holy, holy, holy is the Lord!
Holy, holy, holy, holy is his word!
He has no beginning, he has always been
Always is and ruleth, always he will be.

Bitte um Segen

Pray For Blessings

1. Jeszt. o Va-ter, seg-ne mich! Je-su Kreuz umschlinge ich.
2. Jetzt ist's an-ge-neh-me Zeit, Alles, al-les ist be-reit!

Nimm' hinweg all' meine Schuld, Heile mich in Deiner Huld.
Herr, ich trau-e auf Dein Wort, Segne mich, Du treuer Hort!

Seg-ne mich

seg-ne mich! Jetzt o Va-ter, seg-ne mich!

3. Jetzt, um Christi willen, Jetzt,
   Da Dein Tisch mir ist gesetzt,
   Gib mir Lebensbrot und Wein,
   Mache mich von Sünden rein!

4. Jetzt seh' ich, wie nie zuvor,
   Gläubig, Herr, zu Dir empor!
   Jesus, meiner Seele Schatz,
   Bei Dir ist der schönste Plastz!

1. Oh, dear Father bless me now
   Jesus to Thy cross I bow
   Take away all of my sin
   Make me pure without, within.

2. Now it is the proper time
   All prepared, Oh Jesus mine
   As I trust in all thy word
   Bless me now, oh, gracious Lord.

3. Now through Christ his love I share
   Here the table spread with care
   Give me living bread and wine
   So that I'll be ever thine.

Chorus:
   Bless me now, bless me now,
   Now, oh Father, bless me now!

Unsern Ausgang segne Gott, unsern Eingang gleichermassen;
segne unser täglich Brot, segne unser Tun und Lassen. Segne uns
mit sel'gem Sterben und mach uns zu Himmelserben.

Der grosse Arzt

The Great Physician

1. Der gro-sse Arzt ist jetzt uns nah, Der lie-be, teu - re Je - sus.
2. Ge - tilgt ist un-sre Sün-den-schuld; Denn dafür büsste Je - sus.
3. Hin-weg ist al - le Sün-den - pein; Das macht der teure Je - sus!

Er ist mit sei - nem Tro-ste da. Kein Heil ist au-sser Je - su!
Er führt zum Him-mel uns voll Huld; Dort krönt uns un-ser Je - sus!
In Ihm fand ich mein Heil al - lein, Ja vol-les Heil, o Je - su!

Chorus:

Horch, wie tönt der En-gel sang! O welch sü - sser Ju - bel-klang!

pp

Sing' mein Herz, mit freud'-gem Drang: Je-sus, Je - sus, Je - sus!

1. The great Physician now is near, The sympathizing Jesus;
   He speaks the drooping heart to cheer, O hear the voice of Jesus.

Chorus:
   Sweetest note in seraph song; Sweetest name on mortal tongue;
   Sweetest carol ever sung, Jesus blessed Jesus.

2. Your many sins are all forgiv'n; Oh, hear the voice of Jesus;
   Go on your way in peace and heav'n, and wear a crown with Jesus.

3. His name dispels my guilt and fear; No other name but Jesus;
   Oh, how my soul delights to hear the precious name of Jesus.

27

Der schönste Name

Take The Name Of Jesus With You

1. O wie süss klingt Jesu Name! O wie heilt er allen Schmerz!
2. Lasst uns ziehn in Jesu Namen, Er ist eine gute Wehr;
3. Singt mit Macht in Jesu Namen, Seinen Ruhm mit Mut bezeugt,

Und wie bringt er Fried' und Freude Jedem kindlich gläub'gen Herz!
In Ihm werden wir besiegen Unsrer Feinde ganzes Heer!
Bis wir zu der Schar gelangen Die gekrönt sich vor Ihm neigt.

Chorus

O wie süss es erklingt, Wenn ein Herz von Jesu singt!

O wie süss es erklingt

O wie süss es erklingt, Wenn ein Herz von Jesu singt!

O wie süss, O wie süss es klingt,

28

1. Take the name of Jesus with you,
   Child of sorrow and of woe —
   It will joy and comfort give you,
   Take it then where'er you go.

Chorus:
   Precious name, O how sweet!
   Hope of earth and joy of heav'n,
   Precious name, O how sweet —
   Hope of earth and joy of heav'n.

2. Take the name of Jesus ever
   As a shield from every snare;
   If temptations 'round you gather,
   Breathe that holy name in pray'r.

3. At the name of Jesus bowing,
   Falling prostrate at His feet,
   King of kings in heav'n we'll crown Him
   When our jouney is complete.

Mein Erlöser lebt

I Know That My Redeemer Lives

1. I know that my Redeemer lives;
   What comfort this sweet sentence gives!
   He lives, He lives, who once was dead;
   He lives, my ever-living Head.

2. He lives triumphant from the grave,
   He lives eternally to save,
   He lives all-glorious in the sky,
   He lives exalted there on high.

3. He lives to bless me with His love,
   He lives to plead for me above,
   He lives my hungry soul to feed,
   He lives to help in time of need.

Der herrliche Strom

Shall We Gather At The River

1. Sammeln wir am Strom uns al - le,   Wo die En - gel war - ten schon
2. Dort, wo an des Stroms Ge-sta-de   Sich die Sil - ber-wel - le bricht,
3. An dem Sil - ber-strom im Le - ben Schliesst sich un - ser Pil-ger-lauf,

Und die Was - ser wie Kri - stal - le   Flie - ssen hin vor Got - tes Thron?
Prei-sen e - wig wir die Gna - de   An dem Tag voll Glanz und Licht.
Und des Her-zens hei - lig Be - ben   Geht in Won-ne - jub - bel auf!

Chorus

Ja, wir sammeln uns am Strome, Dem herr-lichen, dem herr-li-chen Strome;

Sammeln uns mit Hei - li - gen am Stro-me, der hin-fliesst vor Got - tes Thron.

1. Shall we gather at the river
   Where bright angel feet have trod;
   With its crystal tide forever
   Flowing by the throne of God?

2. On the margin of the river,
   Washing up its silver spray,
   We will walk and worship ever,
   All the happy, golden day.

Chorus:
   Yes, we'll gather at the river;
   The beautiful, the beautiful river —
   Gather with the saints at the river,
   That flows by the throne of God.

3. Soon we'll reach the silver river,
   Soon our pilgrimage will cease;
   Soon our happy hearts will quiver
   With the melody of peace.

Führe du uns, o Jehovah

Guide Me, O Thou Great Jehovah

1. Füh-re du uns, o Je-ho-vah, Pilgernd durch der Wüste Sand.

Wir sind schwach, doch du bist mächtig, Trage uns mit starker Hand.

Him-melsmanna, Himmelsmanna! Speise du dein mattes Volk.

2. Öffne du den ew'gen Felsen,
   Draus das Lebenswasser fliesst.
   Schütz uns mit der Feuersäule,
   Wenn der Feind uns rings umschliesst.
   Grosser Retter, grosser Retter,
   Sei du unser Schild und Hort.

3. Steh'n wir an des Jordan's Ufer,
   Mach' uns durch den Strom die Bahn,
   Dass dein müdes Volk kann kommen
   Ins verheiss'ne Kanaan.
   Dankeslieder, Dankeslieder,
   Steigen dann zu dir empor.

1. Guide me, O Thou great Jehovah,
   Pilgrim thro' this barren land;
   I am weak, but Thou art mighty,
   Hold me with Thy pow'rful hand;
   Bread of heaven, Bread of heaven,
   Feed me till I want no more.

2. Open now the crystal fountain
   Whence the healing waters flow;
   Let the fiery, cloudy pillar
   Lead me all my journey thro';
   Strong Deliv'rer, Strong Deliv'rer,
   Be Thou still my Strength and Shield.

3. When I tread the verge of Jordan,
   Bid my anxious fears subside;
   Bear me thro' the swelling current,
   Land me safe on Canaan's side:
   Songs of praises, Songs of praises,
   I will ever give to Thee.

Er führet mich

He Leadeth Me

1. Er führet mich der Jugend gleich, O Himmelswort, an Trostgold reich!
2. Durch kalte Ne - bel, trübe Nacht, Durch Gärten, wo der Sommer lacht!
3. Wenn hier mein Werk beendet ist, Und Sieg mir winkt durch Jesum Christ;

Auf jedem Pfad, in je-dem Land, Er-hält und führt mich Gottes Hand!
Auf Wogen wild, am grünen Strand Führt mich, es führt mich Gottes Hand!
Durch Todesgraun, auf sich'rer Bahn führt seine Hand mich himmelan.

Chorus

Er führt mich treu, er führt mich fein, An seiner Hand! Tag-aus, Tag-ein;

Sein wahrer Jünger möcht' ich sein, Denn nur mein Herr führt treu und fein.

1. He leadeth me!   Oh! blessed thought,
   Oh! words with heav'nly comfort fraught;
   What-e'er I do, wher-e'er I be,
   Still 'tis God's hand that leadeth me.

Chorus:
   He leadeth me, He leadeth me!
   By His own hand He lead-eth me.
   His faithful follower I would be,
   For by His hand He leadeth me.

2. Sometimes mid scenes of deepest gloom,
   Sometimes where Eden's bowers bloom,
   By waters still, O'er troubled sea,
   Still 'tis God's hand that leadeth me.

3. And when my task on earth is done,
   When by thy grace the victory's won,
   E'en death's cold wave I will not flee,
   Since God through Jordan leadeth me.

Liebster Jesu, wir sind hier

Blessed Jesus, At Thy Word

Liebster Je-su, wir sind hier, Dich und dein Wort anzu hö - ren;
Len-ke Sinnen und Be - gier Auf die süssen Himmels-leh - ren,
Dass die Herzen von der Erden Ganz zu dir ge-zo-gen wer - den!

2. Unser Wissen und Verstand
   Ist mit Finsternis umhüllet
   Wo der Geist, den du gesandt,
   Nicht mit deinem Licht uns füllet;
   Gutes denken, tun und dichten
   Musst du selbst in uns verrichten.

3. O du Glanz der Herrlichkeit,
   Licht vom Licht, aus Gott geboren,
   Mach' uns allesamt bereit,
   Öffne Herzen, Mund und Ohren;
   Unser Bitten, Fleh'n und Singen
   Lass, Herr Jesu, wohl gelingen!

1. Blessed Jesus, at Thy word
   We are gathered all to hear Thee;
   Let our hearts and souls be stirred
   Now to seek and love and fear Thee,
   By Thy teachings, sweet and holy,
   Drawn from earth to love Thee solely.

2. All our knowledge, sense, and sight
   Lie in deepest darkness shrouded
   Till Thy Spirit breaks our night
   With the beams of truth unclouded.
   Thou alone to God canst win us;
   Thou must work all good within us.

3. Glorious Lord, Thyself impart,
   Light of Light, from God proceeding:
   Open Thou our ears and heart,
   Help us by Thy Spirit's pleading;
   Hear the cry Thy people raises,
   Hear and bless our prayers and praises.

Friede mit Gott

It Is Well With My Soul

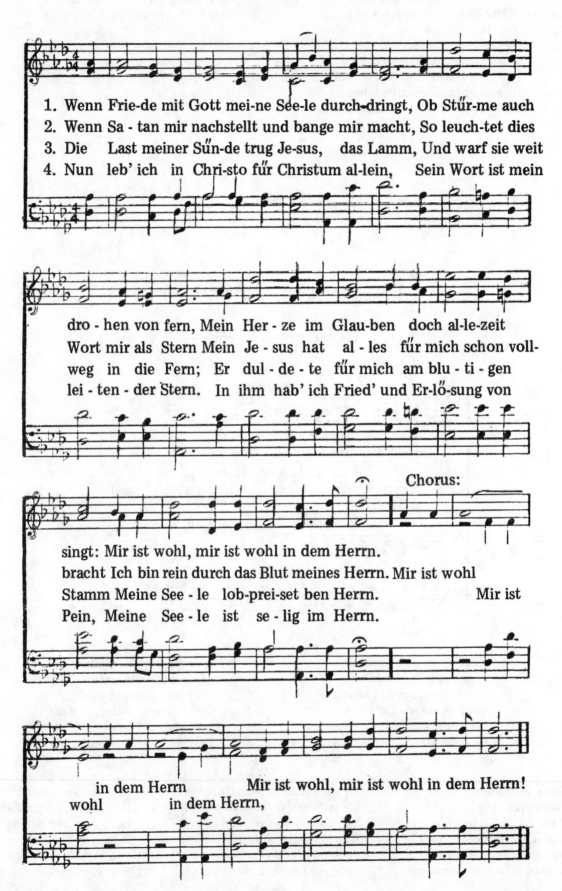

1. Wenn Frie-de mit Gott mei-ne See-le durch-dringt, Ob Stür-me auch
2. Wenn Sa - tan mir nachstellt und bange mir macht, So leuch-tet dies
3. Die Last meiner Sün-de trug Je-sus, das Lamm, Und warf sie weit
4. Nun leb' ich in Chri-sto für Christum al-lein, Sein Wort ist mein

dro - hen von fern, Mein Her - ze im Glau-ben doch al-le-zeit
Wort mir als Stern Mein Je - sus hat al - les für mich schon voll-
weg in die Fern; Er dul - de - te für mich am blu - ti - gen
lei - ten - der Stern. In ihm hab' ich Fried' und Er-lö-sung von

singt: Mir ist wohl, mir ist wohl in dem Herrn.
bracht Ich bin rein durch das Blut meines Herrn. Mir ist wohl
Stamm Meine See - le lob-prei-set ben Herrn. Mir ist
Pein, Meine See - le ist se - lig im Herrn.

Chorus:

in dem Herrn   Mir ist wohl, mir ist wohl in dem Herrn!
wohl   in dem Herrn,

1. When peace, like a river, attendeth my way,
   When sorrows, like seabillows roll;
   Whatever my lot, Thou hast taught me to say,
   It is well, it is well with my soul.

2. Though Satan should buffet, tho' trials should come,
   Let this blest assurance control,
   That Christ hath regarded my helpless estate,
   And hath shed His own blood for my soul.

3. My sin—oh, the bliss of this glorious thought—
   My sin— not in part, but the whole,
   Is nailed to His cross and I bear it no more,
   Praise the Lord, praise the Lord, oh, my soul.

4. And, Lord, haste the day when the faith shall be sight,
   The clouds be rolled back as a scroll,
   The trump shall resound, and the Lord shall descend,
   "Even so,"—it is well with my soul.

Chorus:

It is well   with my soul,
It is well, it is well with my soul.

Ehr' sei dem Vater und dem Sohn

Praise God From Whom All Blessings Flow

Ehr' sei dem Vater und dem Sohn, Dem heilgen Geist auf einem Thron;

Der Hei-li-gen Drei-ei-nig-keit Sei Lob und Preis in E - wig - keit.

Praise God from whom all blessings flow,
Praise Him all creatures here below,
Praise Him above you heavenly host
Praise Father, Son and Holy Ghost.

Gott mit euch

God Be With You

1. Gott, mit euch, bis wir uns wie-der-seh'n! Mög er ra-tend ob euch
2. Gott, mit euch, bis wir uns wie-der-seh'n! Mög sein Fittich euch be-
3. Gott, mit euch, bis wir uns wie-der-seh'n! Wenn sich Wet-ter-wol-ken

wal-ten,   Euch bei sei-ner Herd er-hal-ten!   Gott mit
de-cken,   Mögt sein Le-bens-brot ihr schme-cken!   Gott mit
tur-men,   Mög sein ew'-ger Arm euch schir-men!   Gott mit

Chorus:

euch, bis wir uns Wie-der-seh'n!   Wie-der-seh'n   Wie-der-

seh'n   Einst vor Got-tes Thron wir steh'n   Wie-der-

seh'n   Wie-der-seh'n!   Gott mit euch, bis wir uns wiederseh'n!

1. God be with you till we meet again!
   By His counsels guide uphold you,
   With His sheep securely fold you;
   God be with you till we meet again!

   Chorus:
   Till we meet!   Till we meet!
   Till we meet at Jesus' feet!
   Till we meet!   Till we meet!
   God be with you till we meet again!

2. God be with you till we meet again!
   'Neath His wings protecting hide you,
   Daily manna still provide you;
   God be with you till we meet again!

3. God be with you till we meet again!
   When life's perils thick confound you,
   Put His arms unfailing round you;
   God be with you till we meet again.

Schönster Herr Jesu

Fairest Lord Jesus

1. Fairest Lord Jesus, Ruler of all nature, O Thou of God and man the Son,
   Thee will I cherish, Thee will I honor, Thou my soul's Glory, Joy and Crown.

2. Fair are the meadows, Fairer still the woodlands, Robed in the blooming garb of spring:
   Jesus is fairer, Jesus is purer, Who makes the woeful heart to sing.

3. Fair is the sunshine, Fairer still the moonlight, And all the twinkling, starry host:
   Jesus shines brighter, Jesus shines purer, Than all the angels heaven can boast.

4. Beautiful Saviour, Lord of the nations, Son of God and Son of Man!
   Glory and honor, praise, adoration, Now and forevermore be Thine!

Heilig, heilig ist der Herr

Holy Is The Lord

1. Hei-lig, hei-lig, hei-lig ist der Herr! Jauchzt ihm, ihr Völker,
2. Lobt ihn Preist ihn! Gebt die Herzen hin! Wäch - ter auf Zi - on,
3. Hei-lig! E - wig! Licht ist sein Ge - wand! Herr ist Je-ho - vah;

rühmt sei-nen Na - men! Bebt, ihr Berge! Brau-se laut, o Meer!
frei es ver - kün - det. Lasst das Wort mit heil'gem Feuer glüh'n,
wer kann ihm glei-chen? Er bleibt Sieger, stark ist sei - ne Hand,

Ruft da - zu, ihr Hü-gel, das A - men. Gnädig und gütig.
Am Al - tar die Fackel ent-zün-det. Preist ihn ihr Engel,
Tod und Sün-de muss vor ihm wei-chen. Wenn wir erwachen

mäch-tig und wei-se, Gross ist Je - ho - vah, Herrscher der Welt!
strah-len - de Helden, Tau - send-mal tausend, be - tet ihn an!
in sei - nem Bil-de, Schauen auch wir ihn, jauchzen ihm zu.

ritard.

Chorus

Hei-lig, hei-lig, hei-lig ist der Herr! Ruft dazu, ihr Hügel, das A - men.

1. Holy, holy, holy is the Lord!
Sing, O ye people, gladly adore Him;
Let the mountains tremble at His word,
Let the hills be joyful before Him;
Mighty in wisdom, boundless in mercy,
Great is Jehovah, King over all.

Chorus:
Holy, holy, holy is the Lord,
Let the hills be joyful before Him.

2. Praise Him praise Him shout aloud for joy!
Watchman of Zion, herald the story;
Sin and death His kingdom shall destroy,
All the earth shall sing of His glory;
Praise Him, ye angels, ye who behold Him
Robed in His splendor, matchless, divine.

3. King Eternal, blessed be His name!
So may His children gladly adore Him;
When in heav'n we join the happy strain,
When we cast our bright crowns before Him;
There in His likeness joyful awaking,
There we shall see Him, there we shall sing.

Heimgang

Going Home

1. Lasst mich gehn, lasst mich gehn, Dass ich Je - sum mö - ge
2. Sü - sses Licht, sü - sses Licht, Son - ne, die durch Wol-ken
3. Ach, wie schön, ach, wie schön Ist der En - gel Lob - ge -
4. Wie wird's sein, wie wird's sein, Wenn ich zieh' in Sa - lem
5. Pa - ra - dies, Pa - ra - dies, Wie ist dei - ne Frucht so

sehen! Mei - ne Seel' ist voll Ver - lan - gen, Ihn auf
bricht! O wann werd' ich da - hin kom-men, Dass ich
tön! Hätt' ich Flü - gel, hätt' ich Flü - gel, Flög' ich
ein? In die Stadt der gold - nen Gas - sen; Herr, mein
süss! Un - ter dei - nen Le - bens - bäu - men Wird uns

e - wig zu um - fan - gen, Und vor Sei - nem Thron zu stehn.
dort mit al - len Frommen Schau' Dein hol-des An - ge - sicht!
ü - ber Tal und Hü - gel Heu - te noch nach Zi - ons Höhn.
Gott, ich kann's nicht fassen, Was das wird für Won - ne sein!
sein als ob wir träu-men; Bring' uns, Herr, ins Pa - ra - dies!

1. Let me go, let me go
   That my Jesus I may know!
   My soul longs to see his face,
   Him forever to embrace,
   Standing there before his throne.

2. Sweetest light, sweetest light,
   Sun that takes away the night!
   When I will arrive up yonder
   Where with all the saints in wonder
   I will see your face so bright.

3. Oh, how glorious, oh, how glorious
   Is the angel's song victorious!
   Had I wings I would take flight
   Over valley and hillside
   Yet today to Zion's hills.

4. What will be, what will be
   When Jerusalem I see!
   Gates of pearls and streets of gold,
   Lord, my God, there to behold
   Wondrous bliss eternally!

5. Paradise, paradise
   Oh, your fruits are sweet and nice!
   Under trees of life to rest
   Like a dream of heaven blessed.
   Take us, Lord, to Paradise!

Hier auf Erden bin ich ein Pilger

I'm A Pilgrim

1. Hier auf Er-den bin ich ein Pil-ger, Und mein Pil-gern, und mein
2. Wo die Sonne auf im-mer scheinet, O wie sehn' ich o wie
3. In dem Lande, zu dem ich ge-he, Mein Er-lö-ser, mein Er-

Chorus: Hier auf Er-den bin ich ein Pil-ger, Und mein Pilgern, und mein

FINE.

Pil-gern währt nicht lang; O lass mich zie-hen zu je-nen
sehn' ich mich da-hin! Ich bin ein Wan-d'rer in frem-den
lö-ser ist das Licht. Da ist kein Kum-mer und kein Ver-

Pil-gern Währt nicht lang.

D.C. Chor.

Hö-hen Wo Frie-dens-pal-men auf e-wig we-hen!
Lan-den, Mein Herz ist trau-rig, mein Geist in Ban-den.
der-ben, Da ist kein Ir-ren und auch kein Ster-ben.

1. I'm a pilgrim, and I'm a stranger;
   I can tarry, I can tarry but a night!
   Do not detain me, for I am going,
   To where the streamlets are ever flowing.

   Chorus

   I'm a pilgrim and I'm a stranger,
   I can tarry, I can tarry but a night.

2. Of that country to which I'm going
   My Redeemer, my Redeemer is the light,
   There is no sorrow, nor any sighing,
   Nor any sin there nor any dying.

3. There the sunbeams are ever shining
   Oh! my longing heart, my longing heart is there;
   Here in this country, so dark and dreary,
   I long have wandered forlorn and weary.

Himmelan, nur Himmelan

Heavenward

1.
Him-mel-an, nur him-mel - an, Soll der Wan-del geh'n;
Was die Frommen wünschen, kann Dort erst ganz ge-scheh'n,

Auf Er - den nicht. Freu-de wech-selt hier mit Licht;

Richt' hin - auf zur Herr - lich - keit Dein An - ge - sicht!

2. Himmelan schwing' deinen Geist
Jeden Morgen auf!
Kurz, ach kurz ist, wie du weisst,
Unser Pilgerlauf.
Fleh' täglich neu;
Gott, der mich zum Himmel schuf,
Präg' ins Herz mir den Beruf,
Mach' mich getreu!

3. Halleluja singst auch du,
Wenn du Jesum siehst,
Unter Jubel ein zur Ruh
In den Himmel ziehst.
Gelobt sei er!
Der vom Kreuz zum Throne stieg,
Hilft auch dir zu deinem Sieg:
Gelobt sei er!

2. Heavenward wings spirit mine
Every morning near
Quickly, quickly as you know
Pilgrm journey here.
Pray daily a-new
God who me to heaven calls
In my heart impress thine all
Keep me ever true.

1. Heavenward now heavenward
Must my journey go
What the holy people wish
There shall it be so
On earth not a-glow
Sometimes glad and sometimes sad
Turn to him for glories
Heaven's view does flow.

3. Halleluja sing your best
When Christ you shall see
With much joy you go to rest
Heaven you enter free
Praise to His name
He who from the cross to crown
Helps you to the heaven renown
For godly fame.

Hymne an die Nacht

Hymn to the Night

1. Holy night, o gently pour heaven's peace into my soul.
   Bring this lowly pilgrim rest, soothe his troubles and console.
   Brightly appears a star, greeting me from afar:
   I only long to flee to you, heaven bound.

2. Sounds of golden harps I hear, floating softly like a kiss
   From realms of paradise and from love's eternal bliss.
   Glow ye, o brilliant star, greeting me from afar:
   I only long to flee to you, heaven bound.

Gebete.

Des Morgens, wenn ich früh aufsteh'
und abends, wenn ich schlafen geh',
sehn meine Augen, Herr, auf dich!
Herr Jesus, dir befehl' ich mich.   Amen.

Segne, Vater, unsern Fleiß,
daß wir täglich hier auf Erden,
uns zum Glück und dir zum Preis,
besser und geschickter werden.   Amen.

Schlaf ein mit Gott, mit Gott wach auf,
mit Gott geh' aus und ein;
und alles, alles, was du tust,
das tu mit Gott allein.

Ich bete an die Macht der Liebe

To Worship Thee The Power Of Love

1. To worship thee, the power of love
   Which in Christ Jesus was revealed
   And bow in rev'rence to Him above
   Who me from lowly dust has raised.
   I shall therefore your love fulfilling
   Direct my ways into your keeping.

2. As you have shown your loving favor
   Now does my heart yearn after thee
   Your gentle love my secure treasure
   That gives me strength and comforts me
   Your faithful love, your blessed being
   With me your grace forever sharing.

3. O Jesus may your name remaining
   My heart in humble faith receive.
   May your kind love and gentle caring
   Within my soul and spirit live.
   In word and deed and all my doing
   You, Jesus Lord, I will be serving.

Ich weiss, dass mein Erlöser lebt

I Know That My Redeemer Lives

1. Ich weiss dass mein Er-lö-ser lebt, Der mir den
2. Wohl hab ich kei-nen Lohn ver-dient, Auf ihn ver-
3. O Je-su Chri-ste, Got-tes Lamm, Du kamst aus
4. Bald en-det hier mein Pil-ger-lauf, Du öff-nest

D. C.- Bald kommst du, Herr, und rufst mir zu: Ge-treu-er

Him-mel auf-ge-tan. Wenn auch mein Herz im Kam-pfe bebt,
trau' ich ganz al-lein. Er ist's der mich mit Gott ver-sühnt,
heil'-gen Him-mels-höhn, Und starbst für mich am Kreu-zes-stamm;
mir das Him-mels-thor: Dann schwing ich mich zu Je-su auf,

Knecht, geh' ein zur Ruh'! Bald kommst du, Herr, und rufst mir zu:

FINE. Chorus

Einst nimmt er mich in Gna-den an.
Sein Blut wäscht mich von Sün-den rein.
Nun kann auch ich vor Gott be-stehn.
Zur ew'-gen Herr-lich-keit em-por.

Drum ist in die-ser

Ge-treu-er Knecht, geh' ein zur Ruh'!

D.C.

Welt all-hier Mein Wan-del, Je-su, schon mit dir.

1. I know that my Redeemer lives; What comfort this sweet sentence gives!
He lives, He lives, who once was dead; He lives, my ever living head.
He lives to bless me with His love, He lives to plead for me above,
He lives, my hungry soul to feed, He lives to bless in time of need.

2. He lives to grant me rich supply, He lives to guide me with His eye.
   He lives to comfort me when faint, He lives to hear my soul's complaint.
   He lives to silence all my fears, He lives to wipe away my tears,
   He lives to calm my troubled heart, He lives all blessings to impart.

3. He lives, my kind, wise, heav'nly friend, He lives, and loves me to the end,
   He lives, and while He lives I'll sing. He lives, my Prophet, Priest and King.
   He lives, and grants me daily breath, He lives, and I shall conquer death,
   He lives, my mansion to prepare, He lives to bring me safely there.

4. He lives, all glory to His name! He lives, my Jesus, still the same;
   O the sweet joy this sentence gives, "I know that my Redeemer lives!"
   He lives, all glory to His name! He lives, my Jesus, still the same;
   O the sweet joy this sentence gives, "I know that my Redeemer lives!"

Tischgebete

Vor dem Essen: Herr Gott, himmlischer Vater, segne
uns und diese deine Gaben, die wir von deiner milden Güte
zu uns nehmen, durch Jesum Christum, unsern Herrn. Amen

Komm, Herr Jesu! Sei unser Gast,
Und segne, was du uns bescheret hast! Amen.

Aller Augen warten auf Dich, Herr, und du gibst ihnen ihre
Speise zu seiner Zeit. Du tust deine milde Hand auf und sättigst
alles, was da lebet, mit Wohlgefallen. Amen.

Segne, Vater, diese Speise, uns zur Kraft
und dir zum Preise. Amen.

Nach dem Essen: Wir danken dir, Herr Gott, himmlischer
Vater, durch Jesum Christum, unsern Herrn, für alle deine Gaben
und Wohltaten, der du lebest und regierest in Ewigkeit. Amen.

Wir danken dir, Herr Jesu Christ,
Dass du unser Gast gewesen bist.
Bleib du bei uns, so hat's nicht Not,
Du bist das rechte Lebensbrot. Amen.

Jesus liebt mich ganz gewiss

Jesus Loves Me.

1. Je - sus liebt mich ganz ge-wiss, Weil man's in der Bi-bel liest;
2. Gab für mich sein teu-res Blut, Him-mels-pfor-ten auf mir tut,
3. Je - sus liebt mich in - nig-lich; Bin ich traurig, schwach und siech,

Kind-lein kommt zum lie-ben Christ, Weil es schwach, er mäch-tig ist.
Wa-schet mich von Sün-den rein, Trägt sein klei-nes Lamm hinein
Kommt er zu mir bei der Nacht, Und an meinem Bettlein wacht.

Chorus:

O, Je - sus liebt mich, O, Je - sus liebt mich,

O, Je - sus liebt mich, Denn mei - ne Bi - bel sagt's.

1. Jesus loves me! This I know,
   For the Bible tells me so;
   Little ones to him belong;
   They are weak, but he is strong.

Chorus:
   Yes, Jesus loves me; Yes, Jesus loves me!
   Yes, Jesus loves me; The Bible tells me so!

2. Jesus loves me! He who died,
   Heaven's gate to open wide!
   He will wash away my sin,
   Let his little child come in.

3. Jesus take this heart of mine,
   Make it pure and wholly Thine;
   Thou hast bled and died for me,
   I will henceforth live for Thee.

46

Jesus nimmt die Sünder an

Christ Receiveth Sinful Men

1. Je-sus nimmt die Sünder an, Führt sie auf die Lebensbahn;
2. Bist du noch so weit verirrt, Es sucht dich der treu-e Hirt,
3. Hier kannst du die Liebe seh'n. Höher als des Himmels Höh'n,

Hier ist, der sie ret-ten kann: Je-sus nimmt die Sünder an.
Weil er dich nicht lassen kann; Je-sus nimmt die Sünder an.
Tie-fer als man denken kann; Je-sus nimmt die Sünder an.

Chorus:

Herr, ich weiss es, du bist mein Und ich bin auf e-wig dein, Freudig sag' ich's Je-der-mann, Je-sus nimmt die Sün-der an.

1. Sinners Jesus will receive; Sound this word of grace to all
   Who the heav'nly pathway leave, All who linger all who fall.

2. Come, and he will give you rest; Trust him for his word is plain;
   He will take the sin-ful-lest; Christ receiveth sinful men.

3. Now my heart condemns me not, Pure before the law I stand;
   He who cleansed me from all spot Satisfied its last demand.

Chorus:

Sing it o'er and o'er again; Christ receiveth sinful men;
Make the message clear and plain: Christ receiveth sinful men.

Komm zu dem Heiland

Come To The Savior

1. Komm zu dem Hei-land, kom-me noch heut! Folg' sei-nem
2. Komm, o mein Kind und hö-re sein Wort, Gib ihm dein
3. Glau-be nur fest, der Herr nimmt dich an! O fühlst du

Wort, jetzt ist es noch Zeit! Er ist uns nah, zum Seg-nen be-reit,
Herz und folg ihm so-fort! Er ist ein sich-rer, e-wi-ger Hort;
ihn nicht jetzt dir schon nahn? Mit Lieb' und Gnad' will Er dich um-fah'n,

Chor.

Und ruft so freundlich komm!
Drum mach dich auf und komm! Herrlich, herrlich wird es einmal sein,
Komm nur, o Sün-der, komm!

Wenn wir ziehn von Sün-de frei und rein, In das ge-

lob-te Ka-na-an ein. Je-su, sieh her: Ich komm!

1. Come to the Saviour, make no delay;
   Here in His word He's shown us the way;
   Here in our midst He's standing today,
   Tenderly saying, "Come"!

Chorus:
   Joyful, joyful will the meeting be,
   When from sin our hearts are pure and free;
   And we shall gather, Saviour, with Thee,
   In our eternal home.

2. "Suffer the children"! Oh, hear His voice,
   Let ev'ry heart leap forth and rejoice,
   And let us freely make Him our choice;
   Do not delay, but come.

3. Think once again, He's with us today;
   Heed now His blest commands, and obey;
   Hear now His accents tenderly say,
   "Will you, my children, come?"

48

Mehr von dem Heiland

More About Jesus

1. Mehr von des Heilands Lieb und Gnad, Mehr von dem Heils und Liebesrat
2. Mehr von der Wahrheit festem Wort, Mehr von der Gnade treuem Hort,
3. Mehr von dem sel'gen Va - ter - land, Heimwärts zu geh'n an Jesu hand,

Mehr von dem Wesen meines Herrn, Mehr von dem Heiland wüsst ich gern.
Mehr von der Liebe hellem Stern, Mehr von dem Heiland wüsst ich gern.
Immer zu fol - gen treu dem Herrn, Mehr von dem Heiland wüsst ich gern.

Chorus:

Mehr, mehr von dem Hei-land, Mehr, mehr von dem Hei-land,

Mehr von der Liebe meines Herrn, Mehr von dem Heiland wüsst ich gern.

1. More about Jesus would I know,
   More of His grace to others show;
   More of His saving fullness see,
   More of His love who died for me.

Chorus:
   More, more about Jesus,
   More, more about Jesus,
   More of His saving fullness see,
   More of His love who died for me.

2. More about Jesus let me learn,
   More of His holy will discern.
   Spirit of God, my teacher be,
   Showing the things of Christ to me.

3. More about Jesus; on His throne,
   Riches in glory all His own;
   More of his kingdom's sure increase;
   More of His coming Prince of Peace.

O heil'ger Geist, kehr' bei uns ein

O Holy Ghost Be Our Guest

1. O heil'-ger Geist, kehr' bei uns ein Und lass uns dei-ne Wohnung sein,
   Du Himmelslicht, lass deinen Schein Bei uns und in uns kräf-tig sein,

O komm, du Herzenssonne!
Zu ste-ter Freud' und Wonne!] Son - ne, Won - ne, Himmlisch Le-ben

Willst du ge-ben, Wenn wir be-ten; Zu dir kommen wir ge - tre - ten.

2. Du Quell, d'raus alle Weisheit fliesst,
   Die sich in fromme Seelen giesst,
   Lass deinen Trost uns hören;
   Dass wir in Glaubenseinigkeit
   Auch andre in der Christenheit
   Dein wahres Zeugnis lehren!
   Höre, lehre,
   Dass wir können
   Herz und Sinnen
   Dir ergeben,
   Dir zum Lob und uns zum Leben!

3. Gib Kraft und Nachdruck deinem Wort,
   Lass es wie Feuer immerfort
   In unsern Seelen brennen;
   Dass wir uns mögen nimmermehr
   Von deiner weisheitreichen Lehr
   Und treuen Liebe trennen!
   Schenke, senke,
   Deine Güte
   Ins Gemüte,
   Dass wir können
   Christum unsern Heiland nennen!

4. Gib, dass in reiner Heiligkeit
   Wir führen unsre Lebenszeit,
   Sei unsers Geistes Stärke;
   Dass uns hinfort sei unbewusst
   Die Eitelkeit, des Fleisches Lust
   Und seine toten Werke!
   Rühre, führe
   Unser Sinnen
   Und Beginnen
   Von der Erden,
   Dass wir Himmelserben werden!

1. O holy ghost be our guest,
   Let us be with your presence blessed,
   Forever be our gladness.
   You heavenly light, your shining ray
   Fill our heart, around us stay,
   Dispelling all our sadness.
   Pleasures, treasures, life worth living
   You are giving us in prayer.
   We are coming now before you.

2. O fount from which all wisdom flows,
   In humble souls increases and grows,
   Our comfort when we're feeble.
   Grant that we may united stand,
   Spreading your truth across the land
   To all your many people.
   Hear us, teach us, that with our heart
   And power we are serving,
   Praising you with faith unswerving.

3. Lend strength and power to your word
   That it like fire bright and hot
   In our souls be burning.
   That never, never from your love
   Guided by wisdom from above
   Away from you we're turning
   Goodness, kindness now is flowing
   And bestowing us with blessing.
   Christ our Lord we are confessing!

4. Help that we live in holiness
   And let our ordered lives confess
   Your strength we are receiving
   Make us in our aim steadfast
   That we from vanity and lust
   Forever take our leaving.
   Lead us, guide us in our thinking
   And our living, God, our Father,
   Heirs to be with Christ our Brother.

Halleluja! schöner Morgen

Hallelujah! Lovely Morning

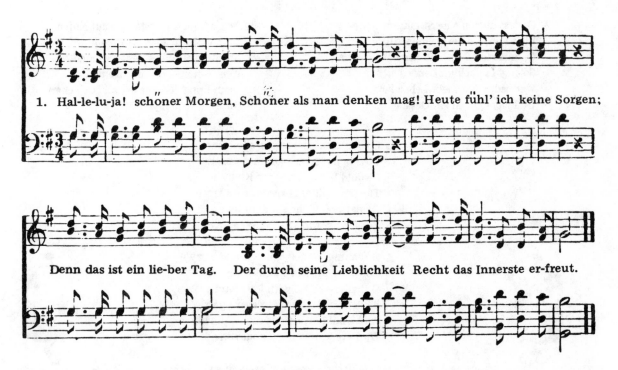

2. Ach, wie schmeck ich Gottes Güte,
   Recht als einen Morgentau,
   Da mein sehnendes Gemüte
   Wandelt auf der grünen Au.
   Da hat wohl die Morgenstund
   Edlen Schatz und Gott im Mund.

3. Herr, ermuntre meine Sinnen
   Und bereite selbst die Brust;
   Lass mich Lehr und Trost gewinnen,
   Gib zu Deinem Manna Lust,
   Dass mir Deines Wortes Schall
   Tief im Herzen widerhall.

4. Segne Deiner Knechte Lehren,
   Oeffne selber ihren Mund.
   Mach mit allen die Dich hören,
   Heute Deinen Gnadenbund.
   Dass wenn man hier bet't und singt
   Solches in Dein Herze dringt.

51

O, dass ich tausend Zungen hätte

O for a Thousand Tongues to Sing

O, dass ich tau-send Zun-gen hät - te Und ei-nen
1. So stimmt' ich da-mit um die Wet - te Aus al-ler-

tau - send - fa - chen Mund!
tief - stem Her-zens-grund   Ein Lob - lied nach dem an-dern

an Von dem, was Gott an mir ge - - tan!

2. O, dass doch meine Stimme schallte
   Bis dahin, wo die Sonne steht!
   O, dass mein Blut mit Jauchzen wallte,
   Solang' es noch im Laufe geht!
   War' jeder Puls mein Leben lang
   Und jeder Odem ein Gesang!

3. Ach, nimm das arme Lob auf Erden,
   Mein Gott, in allen Gnaden hin.
   Im Himmel soll es besser werden,
   Wenn ich bei deinen Engeln bin.
   Dann bring' ich mit der sel'gen Schar
   Dir ewig Halleluja dar!

1. O for a thousand tongues to sing
   To sing my great redeemer's praise
   I would then glorify my King
   The triumph of His wondrous grace
   One after one the songs of love
   For me has sung from God above.

2. O that my humble voice would carry
   To where the sun warms every heart
   O that my blood with joy could answer
   While it still flows with every part
   And would each pulse my whole life long
   With every breath a joyous song.

3. O take the empty praise on this earth
   For God in every way to bear
   In Heav'n it will have more worth
   When I am with His angels there
   Then I will come with blessed love
   For everlasting peace above.

Selig in Jesu Armen

Safe in the Arms of Jesus

1. Se - lig in Je - su Ar - men, si - cher an Sei - ner Brust,
2. Se - lig in Je - su Ar - men, fer - ne von Leid und Not,
3. Je - sus, Du hast ver - gos - en ja auch für mich Dein Blut:

Ruhn in der Lie-be Schat-ten: See - le welch' heil'-ge Lust!
Welt-lust du lockst ver-geb-lich, Sün-de ich bin dir tot!
Wohl ist mein Haus ge-bor-gen, weil's auf dem Fel-sen ruht.

Horch! aus der Fer-ne klin-get En - gel - ge - sang so hehr,
Frei von des Zwei-fels Ban-den, wei-chen muss je - der Feind;
Still will ich hier nun har-ren, wei-chen muss bald die Nacht,

Ü - ber die sel'-gen Flu-ren, ü - bers kri-stall-ne Meer.
Fliesst auch noch manche Trä-ne, bald hab' ich aus-ge - weint!
Bald wird der ew'ge Mor - gen leuch-ten in gold-ner Pracht.

1. Safe in the arms of Jesus, Safe on His gentle breast,
   There by His love o'er shaded Sweetly my soul shall rest.
   Hark! 'tis the voice of angels, Borne in a song to me,
   Over the fields of glory, Over the Jasper sea.

2. Safe in the arms of Jesus, Safe from corroding care,
   Safe from the world's temptations, Sin cannot harm me there.
   Free from the blight of sorrow, Free from my doubts and fears;
   Only a few more trials, Only a few more tears!

3. Jesus, my heart's dear refuge, Jesus has died for me;
   Firm on the Rock of Ages Ever my trust shall be.
   Here let me wait with patience, Wait till the night is o'er;
   Wait till I see the morning Break on the golden shore.

Sel'ge Gewissheit

Blessed Assurance

1. Sel'-ge Ge-wiss-heit, Je - sus ist mein. Nun kann erst recht ich des
2. Sü-sse Er-ge-bung, himmli-sche Freud, Ist man dem Hei - lan-de
3. Se - li - ger Frie-de, hei - li - ge Rast Je - sus be-wahrt mich und

Le - bens mich freu'n. Er - be des Him - mels, e-wig be - glückt
völ - lig ge - weiht; Gött-li-cher Frie - de füllt mei-ne Brust,
trägt mei - ne Last; Glücklich wer des-sen si-cher darf sein:

Chorus:

Wie schon der Vor-schmack wonnig ent - zückt!
Sei - ne Ge - bo - te sind mei-ne Lust. Dies ist mein ew'-ger
Je - su ge - hör' ich, Je - sus ist mein.

Ju-bel-ge-sang, Je-sum ich preis' mit freu-di-gemDrang; Dies ist mein

ew'-ger Ju-bel-ge-sang, Je-sum ich preis' mit freu-di-gemDrang.

1. Blessed assurance, Jesus is mine! O what a foretaste of glory devine!
   Heir of salvation, purchase of God, Born of His Spirit, washed in His blood.

   Chorus:

   This is my story, this is my song, Praising my Saviour all the day long;
   This is my story, this is my song, Praising my Saviour all the day long.

2. Perfect submission, perfect delight, Visions of rapture now burst on my sight!
   Angels descending, bring from above, Echoes of mercy, whispers of love.

3. Perfect submission, all is at rest, I in my Saviour am happy and blest;
   Watching and waiting, looking above, Filled with His goodness, lost in His love.

Die Gnade unsers Herrn Jesu Christi

The Grace of Our Lord Jesus Christ

The grace of our Lord Jesus Christ
and the love of God and the
communion of the Holy Spirit
be with us always. Amen

Sonnenschein des Heils

Sunshine In My Soul

1. Ein hel-ler Son-nen-schein er-giesst Sich mir in's Herz hin-ein;
2. Ein Lied wogt mir in meiner Brust, Ein hel-ler fro-her Sang;
3. Ein neu-er Früh-ling brach mir an, Mit hol-dem Blü-ten-duft;
4. Ein sü̈sses Glück wird mir zu Teil, Ein Trost in al-lem Leid;

Dass es von Won-ne ü̈-ber-fliesst, So hell, so klar, so rein.
Mein Her-ze schwelgt in sel'-ger Lust Und singt aus tiefstem Drang.
Die Son-ne brach des Winters Bann, Ich at-me Früh-lings-lust.
Gott gibt mir hier sein vol-les Heil, Und dort die Se-lig-keit.

Chorus

Son-nen-schein   Son-nen-schein

O du Son-nen-schein des Heils, hel-ler Son-nen-schein des Heils,

Bringst mir Heil in je-dem Kampf und Schmerz;   Der

Lie-bes-blick vom Gna-den-thron, Der bringt Segen in mein Herz.

1. There's sunshine in my soul today,
   More glorious and bright
   Than glows in any earthly sky,
   For Jesus is my light.

2. There's music in my soul today,
   A carol to my King,
   And Jesus, listening, can hear
   The songs I cannot sing.

3. There's springtime in my soul today,
   For when the Lord is near
   The dove of peace sings in my heart,
   The flow'rs of grace appear.

4. There's gladness in my soul today,
   And hope, and praise, and love,
   For blessings which He gives me now,
   For joys "laid up" above.

Chorus   Oh, there's sunshine, blessed sunshine,
           When the peaceful, happy moments roll;
           When Jesus shows His smiling face
           There is sunshine in the soul.

56

Unwandelbar

Kind Words Can Never Die

1. Je - sus, dein teures Wort Bleibt ewig wahr, Zu-flucht und Friedensort,
2. Frei von der Sündenschuld Machst du mein Herz; Herr, dei-ne grosse Huld
3. Lie - be hört nimmer auf, Lie - be be - steht, Wenn auch im Zei-ten-lauf

Selbst in Ge-fahr; Bricht auch die Nacht herein, Leuchtet sein hel-ler Schein
Til-get den Schmerz. Nun bin ich dir geweiht, Zie - he durch Kampf und Streit
Al-les vergeht. Lie - be, die Gott gebot, Siegt ü - ber Grab und Tod,

In al-ler Angst und Pein Tröstlich und klar. Je - sus, dein teures Wort,
Die-ser be-weg - ten Zeit Froh him-melwärts. Frei von der Sün-den-schuld,
Treibt uns in al-ler Not Recht in's Ge-bet. Lie - be hört nimmer auf,

Rit.

Teures Wort, teures Wort, Je - sus, dein teures Wort Bleibt e - wig wahr.
Sündenschuld, Sündenschuld, Frei von der Sündenschuld Machst du mein Herz.
Nimmer auf, nimmer auf, Lie - be hört nimmer auf, Lie - be be - steht.

1. Kind words can never die; Cherished and blessed;
God knows how deep they lie, lodged in the breast;
Like childhood's simple rhymes, said o'er a thousand times
Go thro' all years and climes, the heart to cheer.
Kind words can never die, never, die, never die,
Kind words can never die, no never die.

2. Sweet tho'ts can never die, Tho like the flow'rs
Their brightest hues may fly in wintry hours.
But when a gentle dew gives them their charm anew
With many an added hue, they bloom again.
Sweet tho'ts can never die, never die, never die,
Sweet tho'ts can never die, no never die.

3. Our souls can never die, Tho' in the tomb
We may all have to lie, wrapped in its gloom.
What tho' the flesh decay, souls pass in peace away,
Live thro' eternal day, with Christ above.
Our souls can never die, never die, never die,
Our souls can never die, no never die.

Vorwärts, Christi Streiter

Onward Christian Soldiers

1. Vorwärts, Christi Strei - ter! Auf, zum heil'gen Krieg! Mit dem Kreuzes
2. Got - tes Kreuzgemein - de Ist ein streitbar Heer; Gottes Geist die
3. Vorwärts drum ihr Treuen, Tre - tet in die Reih'n; Stimmt mit kräft gem

zei - chen zie-hen wir zum Sieg. Chri-stus, un - ser Kö - nig,
Waf - fe, Gottes Wort die Wehr. Wir sind nicht zer - tei - let,
Klan - ge In das Lob-lied ein. Lob und Preis und Eh - re

Führet selbst uns an. Folgt dem hohen Führer! Vorwärts, Mann für Mann!
Ei - ne Ritterschaft! Eins in Lieb' und Lehre, Eins in Glaubens-kraft.
Unserm König singt, Und durch ew'ge Zeiten Ihm An-betung bringt.

Chorus

Vor - wärts, Chri - sti Strei - ter! Auf zum heil'- gen Krieg!

Mit dem Kreu - zes - zei - chen Zie - hen wir zum Sieg.

58

1. Onward Christian soldiers! Marching as to war,
   With the cross of Jesus going on before.
   Christ, the Royal Master, Leads against the foe;
   Forward into battle, See His banners go.

2. Like a mighty army Moves the Church of God;
   Brothers, we are treading Where the saints have trod.
   We are not divided, All one body we,
   One in hope and doctrine, One in charity.

Chorus:
   Onward, Christian soldiers! Marching as to war,
   With the cross of Jesus, going on before.

3. Onward, then ye faithful, Join our happy throng,
   Blend with ours your voices, In the triumph song;
   Glory, laud, and honor, Unto Christ the King.
   This thro' countless ages Men and angels sing.

Lobe den Herren, den mächtigen König der Ehren

Praise to the Lord, the Almighty

1. Lo-be den Her-ren, den mäch-ti-gen Kö-nig der Eh - - ren!
   Stimme, du See - le, mit ein zu den himmli - schen Chö - - ren!
2. Lo-be den Her-ren, der al - les so herrlich re - gier - - et,
   der dich auf A - del - ers Fit - ti - chen sich - er ge - füh - - ret,
3. Lo-be den Her-ren, der sichtbar dein Le-ben ge - seg - - net,
   der aus dem Himmel mit Strömen der Lie-be ge - reg - - net.

1. Kommet zu Hauf! Psalter und Harfe wacht auf, lasset den Lobgesang hö - - ren!
2. der dich er - hält, wie es dir selber ge - fällt; hast du nicht dieses ver-spü - - ret!
3. Den - ke da - ran, was der All-mäch-ti-ge kann, der dir mit Lie-be be - ge - - gnet.

1. Praise to the Lord, the Almighty, the King of creation!
   O my soul praise Him, for He is thy health and salvation!
   All ye who hear, Now to His temple draw near;
   Join me in glad adoration!

2. Praise to the Lord, who o'er all things so wondrously reigneth,
   Shelters thee under His wings, yes, so gently sustaineth!
   Hast thou not seen how all thy longings have been
   Granted in what He ordaineth?

3. Praise to the Lord, who doth prosper thy work and defend thee;
   Surely His goodness and mercy here daily attend thee.
   Ponder anew what the Almighty can do,
   If with His love He befriend thee.

Wachet auf, ruft uns die Stimme

Wake, Awake for Night Is Flying

"Wa - chet auf!" ruft uns die Stim - me der Wäch - ter
Mit - ter - nacht heißt die - se Stun - de. Sie ru - fen

sehr hoch auf der Zin - ne, "wach auf, du Stadt Je - ru - sa - lem!"
uns mit hel - lem Mun - de: Wo seid ihr klu - gen Jung-frau - en?

Wohl - auf, der Bräut'-gam kömmt! Steht auf, die Lam-pen nehmt! Hal - le -

lu - ja! Macht euch be-reit zu der Hoch-zeit! Ihr müs-set ihm ent-ge-gen - gehn.

2. Zion hört die Wächter singen;
Das Herz will ihr vor Freude springen
Sie wachet und steht eilend auf.
Ihr Freund kommt vom Himmel prächtig,
Von Gnaden stark, von Wahrheit mächtig;
Ihr Licht wird hell, Ihr Stern geht auf,
Nun komm, du werte Kron',
Herr Jesu, Gottes Sohn!
    Hosianna!
    Wir folgen all'
    zum Freudensaal
Und halten mit das Abendmahl.

3. Gloria sei dir gesungen
Mit Menschen-und mit Engelzungen,
Mit Harfen und mit Cymbeln schön!
Von zwölf Perlen sind die Tore
An deiner Stadt; wir steh'n im Chore
Der Engel hoch um deinen Thron.
    Kein Aug' hat je geseh'n
    Kein Ohr hat je gehört
    Solche Freude;
    Drum jauchzen wir
    Und singen dir
Das Halleluja für and für.

Wake, awake, for night is flying,
The watchmen on the heights are crying;
Awake, Jerusalem, arise!
Midnight hears the welcome voices
And at the thrilling cry rejoices:
Oh, where are ye, ye virgins wise?
The Bridegroom comes, awake!
Your lamps with gladness take!
Hallelujah!
With bridal care yourselves prepare
To meet the Bridegroom, who is near.

2. Zion hears the watchmen singing,
And all her heart with joy is springing
She wakes, she rises from her gloom;
For her Lord comes down all glorious,
The strong in grace, in truth victorious,
Her Star is ris'n, her Light is come.
Now come, Thou Blessed One,
Lord Jesus, God's own Son,
Hail! Hosanna!
The joyful call we answer all
And follow to the nuptial hall.

3. Now let all the heav'ns adore Thee,
Let men and angels sing before Thee,
With harp and cymbal's clearest tone.
Of one pearl each shining portal,
Where, dwelling with the choir immortal,
We gather round Thy radiant throne,
No vision ever brought.
No ear hath ever caught,
Such great glory;
Therefore will we eternally
Sing hymns of praise and joy to Thee.

Gott ist die Liebe

God Is So Loving

1. Gott ist die Lie-be, Lässt mich er-lö-sen; Gott ist die

Refrain

Lie-be, Er liebt auch mich. Drum sag' ich noch ein-mal:

Gott ist die Lie-be, Gott ist die Lie-be, Er liebt auch mich.

1. God is so loving, grants me salvation;
   God is so loving, loves even me.

2. Ich lag in Banden
   Der schnöden Sünden
   Ich lag in Banden
   Und konnt' nicht los.

Chorus
   Thus say I once again, God is so loving;
   God is so loving, loves even me.

3. Dich will ich preisen,
   Du ew'ge Liebe;
   Dich will ich loben,
   So lang' ich bin!

2. I lay in bondage, burdened by sinning;
   I lay in bondage, and never free.

3. Lord I will praise thee, eternally loving;
   Lord I will bless thee, so long I live.

Wenn der Heiland

Precious Jewels

1. Wenn der Hei-land, wenn der Heiland Als Kö - nig er - scheint
2. Er wird sammeln, er wird sammeln Zur hei - li - gen Schar
3. Drum ihr Grossen und ihr Kleinen, Gebt Jesu das Herz!

Und die Sei - nen als Er - lös - te Im Him-mel ver-eint,
All' die See - len, die im Blu - te Sich wu-schen recht klar.
Er macht se - lig, er macht herrlich Er führt himmelwärts!

Chorus

O dann wer-den sie glän-zen, Wie Ster - ne so rein,

In des Hei - lan - des Kro-ne als E - del - ge - stein!

1. When He cometh, when He cometh
   To make up His jewels,
   All His jewels, precious jewels,
   His lov'd and His own.

Chorus:
   Like the stars of the morning,
   His bright crown adorning,
   They shall shine in their beauty,
   Bright gems for His crown.

2. He will gather, He will gather
   The gems for His kingdom;
   All the pure ones, all the bright ones;
   His lov'd and His own.

3. Little children, little children,
   Who love their Redeemer,
   Are the jewels, precious jewels,
   His lov'd and His own.

Wenn der Herr die Seinen rufet

When the Roll Is Called Up Yonder

1. Wenn der ew'ge Morgen taget und wird keine Zeit mehr sein. Wenn in
2. Wenn die Wetter Gottes flammen in dem grossen Weltenbrand, Und Gott
3. Lasst uns doch mit Ernst bedenken jenes Tages Wichtigkeit, Und mit

alle Gräber tönt des Richters Wort! Wenn die Millionen stehen vor den
seine Feinde schrecket "Weichet fort," Aber freundlich denen winket, die da
heilgem Eifer folgen Gottes Wort! Dass wir freudig sagen können; Komme,

Schranken gross und klein, Und der Herr die Seinen rufet, bin ich dort.
steh'n zur rechten Hand; Und der Herr die Seinen rufet, bin ich dort.
Herr, ich bin bereit! Und der Herr die Seinen rufet, bin ich dort.

Chorus.

Wenn der Herr die Seinen ru— fet, Wenn der
Wenn der Herr die Seinen ru-fet, bin ich da,

Herr die Seinen ru— fet, Wenn der
Wenn der Herr die Seinen rufet bin ich da,

Herr die Seinen rufet, Wenn der Herr die Seinen rufet bin ich da.
Wenn der Herr die Seinen rufet,

When the trumpet of the Lord shall sound, and time shall be no more,
And the morning breaks, eternal, bright and fair;
When the saved of earth shall gather over on the other shore,
And the roll is called up yonder, I'll be there.

On that bright and cloudless morning when the dead in Christ shall rise,
And the glory of His resurrection share;
When His chosen ones shall gather to their home beyond the skies,
And the roll is called up yonder, I'll be there.

3. Let us labor for the Master from the dawn till setting sun,
Let us talk of all His wondrous love and care;
Then when all of life is over, and our work on earth is done,
And the roll is called up yonder, I'll be there.

Chorus:
When the roll is called up yonder,
When the roll is called up yonder,
When the roll is called up yonder,
When the roll is called up yonder, I'll be there.

Wie gross bist Du

How Great Thou Art

1. Du gros-ser Gott, wenn ich die Welt be-trach-te, Die Du ge-
2. Wenn mir der Herr in Sein-em Wort be-geg-net, Wenn ich die
3. Wenn ich be-den-ke meine Le-bens-we-ge, Die Gott ge-

schaffen durch Dein Allmachtswort, Wenn ich auf al-le je-ne Wes-en
grossen Gna-den-ta-ten seh', Wie Er das Volk des Ei-gen-tums ge-
brauchte, mich zu Ihm zu ziehn, Und wenn in Sein-em Lichte ich

ach-te, Die Du re-gierst und liebest fort und fort:
seg-net, Wie Er's ge-liebt, beg-nadigt je und je: Dann jauchzt mein
er-wäge, Wie meinem Hei-land ich nun leb' und dien'.

Refrain

Herz Dir, grosser Herrscher, zu: Wie gross bist Du, wie gross bist Du! Dann jauchzt mein

Herz Dir, grosser Herrscher, zu: Wie gross bist Du, wie gross bist Du!

1. O Lord my God, when I in awesome wonder
   Consider all the worlds thy hand hath made;
   I see the stars, I hear the mighty thunder,
   Thy power throughout the universe displayed.

Chorus:

   Then sings my soul, my Savior God, to thee.
   How great thou art! How great thou art!
   Then sings my soul, my Savior God to thee,
   How great thou art! How great thou art!

2. When through the woods and forest glades I wander,
   I hear the birds sing sweetly in the trees;
   When I look down from lofty mountain grandeur
   And hear the brook and feel the gentle breeze;

3. When Christ shall come, with shout of acclamation,
   And take me home what joy shall fill my heart!
   Then I shall bow in humble adoration
   And there proclaim, "My God, how great thou art!"

Wie lieblich ist's hienieden

How Good It Is for Brethren

1. Wie lieb-lich ist's hie-nie-den, Wenn Brü-der treu ge-sinnt
2. Wie Tau vom Himmel nie-der, Auf Got-tes Ber-ge fliesst;
3. Und ein-stens wird er-neu-et Durch sie die heil'-ge Stadt;
4. Und al-les Volk der Er-de Geht nun zum Lichte ein;

In Ein-tracht und in Frie-den Ver-traut bei-sammen sind;
Al-so auf treu-e Brü-der Der Se-gen sich er-giesst;
Was Knecht ist, wird be-frei-et, Und rein, was Fle-cken hat;
Dann wird nur ei-ne Her-de Und nur ein Hir-te sein;

In Ein-tracht und in Frie-den Ver-traut bei-sammen sind;
Al-so auf treu-e Brü-der Der Se-gen sich er-giesst;
Was Knecht ist, wird be-frei-et, Und rein, was Fle-cken hat.
Dann wird nur ei-ne Her-de Und nur ein Hir-te sein.

How good it is for brethren, Who know each other well,
In unity together on this fair earth do dwell,
In unity together on this fair earth do dwell!

As dew from lofty Hermon, Into the Valley flows,
So God upon the brethren, His choicest gifts bestow.
So God upon the brethren, His choicest gifts bestow!

And thro' them He reneweth, That city fair and free,
Where souls, by sin polluted, shall pure and spotless be.
Where souls, by sin polluted, shall pure and spotless be!

And all the chosen people, Shall there His face behold,
And be with Him forever, One Shepherd and one fold.
And be with Him forever, One Shepherd and one fold.

Wir pilgern nach Zion

We're Marching to Zion

1. Stimmt an mit vol-lem Klang Und prei-set Got-tes Sohn; Wir
2. O kommt und wan-dert mit! Wer mit uns Pil-gern reist. Wird
3. Drum fröh-lich ju-bi-liert, Und lasst das Sor-gen sein; Ein

scha-ren uns mit Ju - bel-sang, Wir scharen uns mit Jubel-sang. Um
eh' sein Fuss die Stadt betritt. Wird eh'sein Fuss die Stadt betritt Mit
fro-hes Herz den Pilger ziert, Ein frohes Herz den Pil-ger ziert, Bald

un - sers Va - ter's Thron, Um un - sers Va - ter's Thron.
Man - na schon ge - speist, Mit Man-na schon ge - speist.
geht's in Zi - on ein, Bald geht's in Zi - on ein.

Chorus

Wir pil - gern nach Zi - on! Herr-li-ches, lieb-li-ches Zi - on! Ja,

heimwärts geht es nach Zi - on, Der herr-li-chen, lieb-li-chen Stadt.

66

1. Come we that love the Lord,
   And let your joys be known,
   Join in a song with sweet accord,
   Join in a song with sweet accord,
   And thus surround the throne,
   And thus surround the throne.

2. The hill of Zion yields
   A thousand sacred sweets,
   Before we reach the heav'nly fields,
   Before we reach the heav'nly fields,
   Or walk the golden streets,
   Or walk the golden streets.

Chorus:
   We're marching to Zion,
   Beautiful, beautiful Zion;
   We're marching upward to Zion,
   The beautiful city of God.

3. Then let our songs abound,
   And ev'ry tear be dry;
   We're marching thro' Immanuel's ground,
   We're marching thro' Immanuel's ground,
   To fairer worlds on high,
   To fairer worlds on high.

So nimm denn meine Hände

Take Thou My Hand, O Father

1. So nimm denn meine Hän - de, Und führe mich Bis an mein
2. In Deine Gnade hül - le, Mein schwaches Herz Und mach' es
3. Wenn ich auch gar nichts füh-le, Von Deiner Macht Du führst mich

selig' Ende Und ewiglich! Ich kann allein nicht gehen,
endlich stille In Freud' und Schmerz; Lass ruh'n zu Deinen Füssen
doch zum Ziele Auch durch die Nacht; So nimm denn meine Hände

Nicht einen Schritt; Wo Du wirst geh'n und stehen, Da nimm mich mit.
Dein schwaches Kind, Es will die Augen schliessen Und folgen blind.
Und führe mich Bis an mein selig' Ende Und ewiglich! Amen.

1. Take Thou my hand, O Father
   And lead Thou me,
   Until my journey endeth,
   Eternally.
   Alone I will not wander
   One single day;
   Be Thou my true Companion
   And with me stay.

2. O cover with Thy mercy
   My poor, weak heart!
   Let ev'ry thought rebellious
   From me depart.
   Permit Thy child to linger
   Here at Thy feet,
   And blindly trust Thy goodness
   With faith complete.

3. Though naught of Thy great power
   May move my soul,
   With Thee thru night and darkness
   I reach the goal.
   Take, then, my hands, O Father,
   And lead Thou me
   Until my journey endeth
   Eternally.

Wie schön leuchtet der Morgenstern

The Morning Star

How gloriously the morning star,
With grace and truth from God afar,
Has risen in great splendor!
O tender shepherd, David's Son,
To you, my King, in heaven's throne,
I now my heart surrender!
Lovely, kindly, great and glorious, all victorious,
Rich in giving, high exalted, ever living.

Wo findet die Seele die Heimat, die Ruh

My Soul Seeks for Heaven

1. Wo fin-det die See-le die Hei-mat,die Ruh'? Wer deckt sie mit schützenden Fit-tichen zu? Ach,
bie-tet die Welt keine Freistatt mir an, wo Sün-de nicht herrschen,nicht an-fechten kann?
Nein, nein, nein,nein, hier ist sie nicht, die Hei-mat der See-le ist dro-ben im Licht!

2. Verlasse die Erde, die Heimat zu sehn,
   Die Heimat der Seele, so herrlich, so schön!
   Jerusalem droben, von Golde erbaut,
   Ist dieses die Heimat der Seele, der Braut?
   Ja, ja, ja, ja, dieses allein
   Kann Ruhplatz und Heimat der Seele nur sein.

3. Wie selig die Ruhe bei Jesu im Licht!
   Tod, Sünde und Schmerzen, die kennt man dort nicht.
   Das Rauschen der Harfen, der liebliche Klang,
   Empfängt die Erlösten mit süssem Gesang.
   Ruh', Ruh', Ruh', Ruh', himmlische Ruh'
   Im Schosse des Mittlers, ich eile ihr zu!

1. My soul seeks for Heaven's eternal sweet rest,
   And longs for the sheltering wings of the blest.
   This world holds no pleasure, no blessing for me,
   Where sins overwhelming cast burdens on me.
   Nay, nay, nay, nay. There is no peace
   My homeland in Heaven grants pure light and peace.

2. This earth I must leave, my true home to behold:
   A place where my soul dwells in glory and love,
   My homeland, Jerusalem, city of gold,
   Is this then my true home in heaven above?
   Yea, yea, yea, yea, this is my home,
   A rest place and homeland for my soul above!

3. How blessed is rest with Lord Jesus, my light,
   Death, sin and deep heartache no longer a plight,
   As harps lend their sweet notes, the heavenly throng
   Accepts the redeemed with beauteous song.
   Peace, peace, peace, peace, heavenly peace;
   In the arms of my Saviour, I'll find perfect peace!

The Little Gate to God

In the castle of my soul
Is a little postern gate,
Whereat, when I enter,
I am in the presence of God.
In a moment, in the turning of a thought,
I am where God is.
This is a fact.

The world of men is made of jangling noises.
With God is a great silence.
But that silence is a melody
Sweet as the contentment of love,
Thrilling as a touch of flame.
When I enter into God,
All life has a meaning.
Without asking I know;
My desires are even now fulfilled,
My fever is gone
In the great quiet of God.
My troubles are but pebbles on the road,
My joys are like the everlasting hills.
So it is when I step through the gate of prayer
From time into eternity.
When I am in the consciousness of God,
My fellowmen are not far off and forgotten,
But close and strangely dear.
Those whom I love
Have a mystic value
They shine as if a light were glowing within them.

So it is when my soul steps through the postern gate
In the presence of God.
Big things become small, and small things become great.
The near becomes far, and the future is near.
The lowly and despised is shot through with glory.
God is the substance of all revolutions;
When I am in him, I am in the Kingdom of God
And in the Fatherland of my Soul.

Walter Rauschenbush

Wenn das Leben köstlich gewesen ist,
so ist es Mühe und Arbeit gewesen.

Psalm 90, 10.

His Love

Florence Hinchman

When God created all the earth,
It was His Will that we
Should love our neighbor as ourselves
And live in harmony . . .

No matter what the race of men,
Their color or their creed,
God willed His Love to all alike
For every human need.

No plan was made for war and strife
For man . . . In God's creation
Our heritage is brotherly love
And peace for every nation.

Wohl dem,
der den Herrn
fürchtet,
und auf
seinen Wegen
geht.

Psalm 128, 1.

Der Herr behüte dich
vor allem Übel;
er behüte deine Seele!
Der Herr behüte
deinen Ausgang und Eingang
von nun an bis in Ewigkeit!

Psalm 121, 7-8

Jehovah will keep thee
from all evil;
He will keep thy soul.
Jehovah will keep thy going out
and thy coming in
From this time forth and
forevermore.

Volks-Lieder

Alleweil ka(nn) ma net lustig sei(n)

Never Can One Merry Be

1. Al - le-weil ka(nn) mer net / lu - stig sei(n), / al - le-weil hot mer kei(n) / Freud; / al - le-weil liebt mer sei / Schät - ze - le net, / Schät - ze - le net, / al - le-weil hot mer net / Zeit.

2. Al - le Tag, wo - n-i di / g'se - he han, / han i mei Freud g'het an / dir. / Wenn i en Tag lang di / gar net sieh, / gar net sieh, / kommst mer no schö - ner du / für.

3. Äu - ge - le hot se in / ih - rem Kopf, / grad wie von wei - tem zwei / Stern', / wie der Kar - fun - kel im / O - fe glitzt, / O - fe glitzt, / wie - n-a Licht in der La - tern'.

1. All the time no one can merry be
   All the time no one has glee
   All the time no one his sweetheart loves, sweetheart loves
   All the time no one is free.

2. Every day when I can see you, dear,
   Joy seems my heart to fill.
   Can I not see you a whole day long, whole day long
   Dearer to me you are still.

3. Two sparkling eyes make her face to shine
   Just like two stars from afar
   Just like the flickering fire's flame, fire's flame
   And like a lantern aglow.

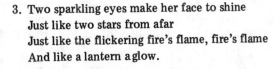

D' Kerbe

Heut isch Kerbe, morga isch Kerbe,
Bis zom Mittwoch Obed,
Wenn ich zu moim Schätzle komm',
No sag' ich: "Guten Obed!"
"Guten Obed, Schätzele,
Sag mer, wo Doi Bettle steht!"
"Henter em Ofa, henter em Eck
Henket drei verissene Röck."

Abschied (Muss i denn)

Departure (Must I Go?)

1. Must I then, must I then to be gone from the town,
    Gone from the town,
  While you, my love, stay here?
  I'll be back, I'll be back, and when I come back,
    When I come back,
  I shall come to you, my dear!
||: Tho' I cannot always with you be,
  Yet you're all the world to me;
  I'll be back, I'll be back, and when I come back,
    When I come back,
  I shall come to you, my dear!:||

2. How you weep, how you weep, now that I must be
    gone,
    I must be gone,
  As though our love were through.
  Everywhere, everywhere are plenty of girls,
    Plenty of girls,
  But to you I'll still be true
||: Never fear, if I another see,
  'T will change my love for you,
  Everywhere, everywhere are plenty of girls,
    Plenty of girls,
  But to you I'll still be true.:||

3. In a year, in a year, when they're gathering the grapes,
    Gathering the grapes,
  I'll return again, you'll see!
  And if then, and if then I'm your heart's dearest still,
    Heart's dearest still,
  Then we can married be.
||: In a year I shall have done my time,
  In a year I shall be free,
  And if then, and if then I'm your heart's dearest still
    Heart's dearest still,
  Then we can married be. :||

Als wir jüngst in Regensburg waren

When Recently in Regensburg

1. Als wir jüngst in Regensburg waren, sind wir über den Strudel gefahren;
2. Und ein Mä-del von zwölf Jahren ist mit über den Strudel gefahren;
3. Und vom ho-hen Ber-ges-schlosse kam auf stol-zem, schwar-zem Rosse

da war'n vie-le Hol-den, die mit-fah-ren woll-ten.
weil sie noch nicht lie-ben kunt, kam sie si-cher über's Stru-dels Grund.
ad-lig Fräu-lein Ku-ni-gund, woll't mit-fahr'n über's Stru-dels Grund.

1.–6. Schwäbi-sche, bay-ri-sche Dirn-del, juch-heirassassa, muß der Schiffsmann fah-ren.

4. Schiffsmann, lieber Schiffsmann mein,
Sollt's denn so gefährlich sein?
Schiffsmann, sag's mir ehrlich,
Ist's denn so gefährlich?

5. Wem der Myrtenkranz geblieben,
Landet froh und sicher drüben;
Wer ihn hat verloren;
Ist dem Tod erkoren.

6. Als sie auf die Mitt' gekommen,
Kam ein großer Nix geschwommen,
Nahm das Fräulein Kunigund,
Fuhr mit ihr in des Strudels Grund.

(Synopsis)

Recently in Regensburg we crossed the River Danube through whirlpools (undertow) on a ferry. Many Swabian and Bavarian girls wanted to cross there. One girl was only 12 years old. Because she has not been in love yet, she made it safely across. Then, riding on a proud black horse, came noble lady Kunigund. She questioned the boatman about the danger of crossing through the whirlpools. His answer: Virgins get across safely; those who aren't virgins drown. When they came to the middle of the river, a big water nymph appeared and pulled Miss Kunigund to the bottom.

Auf de schwäb'sche Eisebahne

On the Swabian Railroad

1. Auf de schwäb'sche Ei-se-bah-ne gibt es vie-le Halt-sta-tio-ne,
   Trul-la, trul-la, trul-la-la, trul-la, trul-la, trul-la-la,

2. Auf de schwäb'sche Ei-se-bah-ne gibt's au vie-le Re-stra-tio-ne,
   Trul-la, trul-la, trul-la-la, trul-la, trul-la, trul-la-la,

3. Auf de schwäb'sche Ei-se-bah-ne dür-fet Küh' und Och-se fah-re,
   Trul-la, trul-la, trul-la-la, trul-la, trul-la, trul-la-la,

Schtue-gert, Ulm und Bi-be-rach, Mek-ke-beu-re, Dur-les-bach.
wo mer essa und trin-ka ka', äl-les, was der Ma-ga mag.
Bue-be, Mäd-le, Weib und Ma, kurz-um älls, was zah-la ka.

4. Wenn e Glöckle tut erklinge,
Tän glei älle z'samma springe,
Aelles, was e Karte hot,
Möcht jetzt mit dem Bahnzug fort.
    Trulla etc.

5. Männer, die im G'sicht ganz bärtig
Schreiet laut: „Jetzt ist es fertig!"
Springet in die Wage nei,
Machet Löchle in d'Karte nei.
    Trulla etc.

6. Auf de schwäb'sche Eisebahne
Wollt emol e Bäuerle fahre,
Goht an d' Kass' und lupft de Hut:
„E Billettle, send so gut!"
    Trulla etc.

7. Einen Bock hat er gekaufet,
Und daß der ihm net verlaufet,
Bindet ihn der gute Ma
Hinte an de Wage na.
    Trulla etc.

8. „Böckle, tu no wacker springe,
Z'fresse werd i dir schau bringe."
Also schwätzt der gute Ma',
Zündt sei Maserpfeifle a.'
    Trulla etc.

9. Als der Zug no wieder staut,
D'r Bauer noch sei'm Böckle schaut,
Find't er bloß no Kopf und Seil
An dem hintre Wageteil.
    Trulla etc.

10. 's packt de Baure a Baurezore,
Nimmt de Geißbock bei de Hore,
Schmeißt en, was er schmeiße ka,
Dem Kondukteur an d'Aura na.
    Trulla etc.

11. Des isch des Lied von sellem Baure,
Der de Geißbock hat verlaure,
Geißbock und sei traurigs End':
Himmel Schtuegert Sapperment.
    Trulla etc.

12. So jetzt wär des Liedle g'songe,
Hot's euch reacht in d' Aure klonge,
Stoßet mit de Gläser a'
Aufs Wohl der schwäb'sche Eisebah'.
    Trulla etc.

Along the Swabian Railroad there are many stops. There are also many restaurants where one can eat and drink to one's heart desire. Cows and oxen can ride on the train, as well as boys, girls, women and men; in short, all who can pay. Once a farmer (peasant) came with a billy goat. He bought a ticket for himself and tied the goat to the last car. "Run fast", he told the goat. "I will bring you food." At the next stop the farmer checked but only found the goat's head on the rope. He became so angry that he took the head and threw it at the conductor. This is the story of the farmer and the sad ending of the goat's life. If you enjoyed this little song, then drink a toast to the Swabian Railroad.

Auf Wiederseh'n

Farewell

fort, _____ denn oh-ne dich _____ ist's · halb so schön, _____ dar -

auf hast du _____ mein Wort. _____ Auf Wie-der-seh'n, _____ auf

Wie-der-seh'n, _____ das ei - ne glau - be mir: Nach - her wird es

_____ noch mal so schön, _____ das Wie-der-seh'n _____ mit dir! _____

1. I love you and you love me,
   That's why I like to have you stay
   But while you have to leave me,
   Listen to what I have to say.

2. We often cannot show it.
   What our heart feels deep inside.
   Although the mouth is quiet
   "Forget me not" the heart confides.

Chorus

Good-bye my dear, come back to me.
Don't stay away too long.
Without you nothing is the same,
Only for you I long.
Good-bye my dear, come back to me.
Believe me, what I say.
And twice as happy we will be
When you return some day.

77

Bier her!

Beer Here!

1. Bier her! Bier her! o-der ich fall um, juchhe! Bier her! Bier her! o - der ich fall um! Soll das Bier im Kel-ler lie-gen, und ich hier die Ohnmacht krie-gen? Bier her! Bier her! o - der ich fall um!

2. Bier her! Bier her! oder ich fall um, juchhe!
Bier her! Bier her! oder ich fall um!
Wenn ich nicht gleich Bier bekumm,
schmeiss ich die ganze Kneipe um!
Drum: Bier her! Bier her! oder ich fall um!

1. Beer here! Beer here! or I shall collapse, o yeah.
Beer here! Beer here! or I shall collapse.
Must the beer stay in the cellar
While I faint and still grow paler?
Beer here! Beer here! or I shall collapse.

2. Beer here! Beer here! or I shall collapse, o yeah.
Beer here! Beer here! or I shall collapse.
If I don't get beer right now,
I will knock the whole place down!
Beer here! Beer here! or I shall collapse.

D'Bäure hot d' Katz verlore

The Farmer's Wife Her Kitten Lost

1. D'Bäu - re hot d'Katz ver - lo - ra, weiß net, wo se ischt, se suecht äl - le Win - ke - le aus: „Mul - le wo bischt?" Se suecht äl - le Win - ke - le aus: „Mul - le, Mul - le wo bischt? 2. Im do!

2. Im Höfle, im Gärtle, was jammert se schwer,
‖: Ruft: "Mulle, liebs Mulle, so gang mer doch her!" :‖

3. Kei Schäfle, kei Kälble, nex was mer begehrt,
‖: Isch mir wie mei Mulle, so lieb und so wert. :‖

4. Was fällt jetzt der Bäure gau siedig heiss ei?
‖: Dort oba auf'm Boda, im Heu drin könnt's sei. :‖

5. Se steiget herzklopfet am Leiterle nauf,
‖: Ka's fast net verschnaufa, machts Falltürle auf. :‖

6. Guckt eine, guckt ausse, jetzt horch, wie se lacht:
‖: "Potz tausig, mei Mulle, a Schläfle hot's g'macht. :‖

7. Jetzt, dass de han gfunde, bin i aber froh!
‖: O Mulle, liebs Mulle, bischt wiederum do! :‖

1. Farmer's wife lost her kitten
   Doesn't know what to do!
   ‖: Looks into all nooks and crannies
   "Pussy, where are you?" :‖

2. Garden and house she searches
   Waiting with fear;
   ‖: Calls, "Pussy, dear Pussy,
   Quickly come back out here." :‖

3. No lamb or little calf
   Or anything here
   ‖: Is worth to me more
   Than my pussy so dear. :‖

4-7 Now the farmer's wife remembers the hay loft.
   With a pounding heart she climbs up the little ladder,
   Looks around and then she laughs,
   "My Pussy is just taking a nap.
   Now that I have found you, my Pussy,
   I am happy again."

79

Die Auserwählte (Mädele ruck, ruck, ruck)

The Chosen One (Come Me Lass)

1. ‖: Come, me lass, slip, slip, slip,
    Slip up and sit beside me;
I am so fond of you,
    Can't you abide me?:‖
      You're so nice and bright,
      You're so pink and white,
      Come, now, won't you stay
      T' while my time away?
      (Repeat first four lines.)

2. ‖: Come, me lass, look, look, look
    In my black eyes, and, we there,
    Your lovely little likeness
    You will see there::‖
      Just look in right well,
      That's where you should dwell;
      Once well in, you'll then
      Not get out again!
      (Repeat first four lines.)

3. ‖: Come, me lass, you, you, you've
    A ring that is worth giving,
Or else, for me, my life
    Is not worth living::‖
      If you won't do so,
      To the wars I go;
      You deny me — why,
      I shall have to die!
      (Repeat first four lines.)

Die Tiroler sind lustig

The Tyrolians are Carefree

1. Die Ti - ro - ler sind lu - stig, die Ti - ro - ler sind
froh, sie trin-ken ein Gläs-chen und ma-chens dann so.

2. Die Tiroler sind lustig,
die Tiroler sind froh,
sie verkaufen ihr Bettchen
und schlafen auf Stroh.

3. Die Tiroler sind lustig,
die Tiroler sind froh,
sie nehmen ein Weibchen
und tanzen dazu.

4. Erst dreht sich das Weibchen,
dann dreht sich der Mann,
sie fassen sich beide
und tanzen zusamm .

1. The Tyrolians are carefree, the Tyrolians are gay
First they drink a little glass full, then they do as they may.

2. The Tyrolians are carefree, the Tyrolians are gay.
Selling swiftly their bedding and sleep in the hay.

3. The Tyrolians are carefree, the Tyrolians are gay
Take a girl for their pastime and go dancing away.

4. First the girl does the turning and then follows the man
And together they're twirling as fast as they can.

Die Schnitzelbank

The Whittle Bench

(The Director Sings the Second and Fourth Lines of Each Verse.)

I.

Ei du schöne, ei du schöne, ei du schöne Schnitzelbank.
Ist das nicht eine Schnitzelbank?
Ja das ist eine Schnitzelbank.
Ist das nicht ein Kurz und Lang?
Ja das ist ein Kurz und Lang.
Kurz und Lang un'er Schnitzelbank.

II

Ei du schöne, ei du schöne, ei du schöne Schnitzelbank.
Ist das nicht ein Hin und Her?
Ja das ist ein Hin und Her.
Ist das nicht 'ne Lichtputzscher?
Ja das ist 'ne Lichtputzscher.
Lichtputzscher, Hin und Her, Kurz und Lang un'er
Schnitzelbank.

III.

Ei du schöne, ei du schöne, ei du schöne Schnitzelbank.
Ist das nicht ein Krumm und Grad?
Ja das ist ein Krumm und Grad.
Ist das nicht ein Wagenrad?
Ja das ist ein Wagenrad.
Wagenrad, Krumm und Grad, Lichtputzscher, Hin und Her,
Kurz und Lang, un'er Schnitzelbank.

IV.

Ei du schöne, ei du schöne, ei du schöne Schnitzelbank.
Ist das nicht ein gold'ner Ring?
Ja das ist ein gold'ner Ring?
Ist das nicht ein schönes Ding?
Ja das ist ein schönes Ding.
Schönes Ding, gold'ner Ring, Wagenrad, Krumm und Grad,
Lichtputzscher, Hin und Her, Kurz und Lang, un'er
Schnitzelbank.

V.

Ei du schöne, ei du schöne, ei du schöne Schnitzelbank.
Ist das nicht der Pferdemeier?
Ja das ist der Pferdemeier.
Sind das nicht sehr grosse Eier?
Ja das sind sehr grosse Eier.
Grosse Eier, Pferdemeier, schönes Ding, gold'ner Ring,
Wagenrad, Krumm und Grad, Lichtputzscher, Hin und Her,
Kurz und Lang, un'er Schnitzelbank.

VI.

Ei du schöne, ei du schöne, ei du schöne Schnitzelbank.
Ist das nicht ein Geissenbock?
Ja das ist ein Geissenbock.
Ist das nicht ein Reifenrock?
Ja das ist ein Reifenrock.
Reifenrock, Geissenbock, grosse Eier, Pferdemeier, schönes
Ding, gold'ner Ring, Wagenrad, Krumm und Grad,
Lichtputzscher, Hin und Her, Kurz und Lang un'er
Schnitzelbank.

VII.

Ei du schöne, ei du schöne, ei du schöne Schnitzelbank.
Ist das nicht 'ne gute Wurst?
Ja das ist 'ne gute Wurst.
Ist das nicht ein grosser Durst?
Ja das ist ein grosser Durst.
Grosser Durst, gute Wurst, Reifenrock, Geissenbock, grosse
Eier, Pferdemeier, schönes Ding, gold'ner Ring, Wagenrad,
Krumm und Grad, Lichtputzscher, Hin und Her, Kurz und
Lang, un'er Schnitzelbank.

VIII.

Ei du schöne, ei du schöne, ei du schöne Schnitzelbank.
Ist das nicht die Herbergsmutter?
Ja das ist die Herbergsmutter.
Ist das nicht 'ne gute Butter?
Ja das ist 'ne gute Butter.
Gute Butter, Herbergsmutter, grosser Durst, gute Wurst,
Reifenrock, Geissenbock, grosse Eier, Pferdemeier, schönes
Ding, gold'ner Ring, Wagenrad, Krumm und Grad,
Lichtputzscher, Hin und Her, Kurz und Lang, un'er
Schnitzelbank.

IX.

Ei du schöne, ei du schöne, ei du schöne Schnitzelbank.
Ist das nicht ein grosser Fisch?
Ja das ist ein grosser Fisch.
Ist das nicht ein kleiner Tisch?
Ja das ist ein kleiner Tisch.
Kleiner Tisch, grosser Fisch, gute Butter, Herbergsmutter,
grosser Durst, gute Wurst, Reifenrock, Geissenbock, grosse
Eier, Pferdemeier, schönes Ding, gold'ner Ring, Wagenrad,
Krumm und Grad, Lichtputzscher, Hin und Her, Kurz
und Lang, un'er Schnitzelbank.

X.

Ei du schöne, ei du schöne, ei du schöne Schnitzelbank.
Ist das nicht ein Besenstiel?
Ja das ist ein Besenstiel.
Ist das nicht ein Aut'mobil?
Ja das ist ein Aut'mobil.
Aut'mobil, Besenstiel, kleiner Tisch, grosser Fisch, gute
Butter, Herbergsmutter, grosser Durst, gute Wurst,
Reifenrock, Geissenbock, grosse Eier, Pferdemeier, schönes
Ding, gold'ner Ring, Wagenrad, Krumm und Grad,
Lichtputzscher, Hin und Her, Kurz und Lang, un'er
Schnitzelbank.

XI.

Ei du schöne, ei du schöne, ei du schöne Schnitzelbank.
Ist das nicht ein Herbergsvater?
Ja das ist ein Herbergsvater.
Ist das nicht ein grauer Kater?
Ja das ist ein grauer Kater.
Grauer Kater, Herbergsvater, Aut'mobil, Besenstiel, kleiner
Tisch, grosser Fisch, gute Butter, Herbergsmutter, grosser
Durst, gute Wurst, Reifenrock, Geissenbock, grosse Eier,
Pferdemeier, schönes Ding, gold'ner Ring, Wagenrad,
Krumm und Grad, Lichtputzscher, Hin und Her. Kurz und
Lang, un'er Schnitzelbank.

XII.

Ei du schöne, ei du schöne, ei du schöne Schnitzelbank.
Ist das nicht ein Affeng'sicht?
Ja das ist ein Affeng'sicht.
Ist das nicht ein helles Licht?
Ja das ist ein helles Licht.
Helles Licht, Affeng'sicht, grauer Kater, Herbergsvater,
Aut'mobil, Besenstiel, kleiner Tisch, grosser Fisch, gute
Butter, Herbergsmutter, grosser Durst, gute Wurst,
Reifenrock, Geissenbock, grosse Eier, Pferdemeier, schönes
Ding, gold'ner Ring, Wagenrad, Krumm und Grad,
Lichtputzscher, Hin und Her, Kurz und Lang, un'er
Schnitzelbank.
Ei du schöne, ei du schöne, ei du schöne Schnitzelbank.

(ad lib.)

Droba auf der rauha Alb

Out Upon the Rugged Alb

1. Dro-ba auf der rau-ha Alb ju-bei-di, ju-bei-da, wie ma-chet's da dia
2. Dro-ba auf der rau-ha Alb ju-bei-di, ju-bei-da, wie ma-chet's da dia
3. Dro-ba auf der rau-ha Alb ju-bei-di, ju-bei-da, wie ma-chet's da dia

Bau-ra all, ju-bei-di-hei-da? Se lau-fet d'Fur-cha auf und ab und
Wirts-leut all, ju-bei-di-hei-da? O-ba schüt-tet's Was-ser nei und
Bäk-ker all, ju-bei-di-hei-da? Do a Eck-le, dort a Eck-le,

flu-chet d'Stern vom Him-mel rab. Ju-bei-di und ju-bei-da, ju-bei-di ei
un-ta geit's da ro-ta Wei.
langt scho wieder a Sech-ser-weck-le.

tra-le-ra, ju-bei-di und ju-bei-da, ju-bei-di-hei-da.

4. Droba . . . Schreiner all?
   Se hoblet Spä und machet Bretter,
   des geht grad wie's Donnerwetter.

5. Droba . . . Schneider all?
   Do a Fleckle, dort a Fleckle,
   z'letzta geit's a Kenderjäckle.

6. Droba . . . Maurer all?
   Se laufet's Leiterle auf und a
   und gucket, ob's net zwolfe schla!

This song makes fun of the people who live in the mountains of Württemberg — the Swabian Alb. It is called "rauh" because of the often harsh and inclement weather. It is not easy to make a living, so the people are very thrifty. Each verse starts with the words, "Up on the harsh Alb"— then the question:

1. What do all the Farmers do? — They run up and down the field (behind the plough) and swear the stars down from the sky.

2. What do all the Innkeepers do? — They add water to the wine.

3. What do all the Bakers do? — Take a little corner from the dough of every roll. This way they get a few extra.

4. What do all the Cabinet Makers do? — They work hard and fast like thunder and lightning.

5. What do all the Tailors do? — Skimp a little here, skimp a little there. In the end there is enough left for a child's jacket.

6. What do all the Brick Layers do? — They run up and down the ladder to see if it isn't noon yet.

84

Du, du liegst mir im Herzen

You, You Live in My Heart Dear

You, You Live In My Heart Dear

1. You, you live in my heart dear; you, you live in my mind.
   You, you give me great heartache; while I to you am so kind.

   Ja, ja, ja, ja, while I to you am so kind.

2. So, so, as I now love thee, so, so, love thou yet me.
   The, the tendermost feelings, have I alone just for thee.

   Ja, ja, ja, ja, have I alone just for thee.

3. Still, still will I be trusting you with your fickle mood,
   Yet, you on me relying, know that my love it is good.

   Ja, ja, ja, ja, know that my love it is good.

4. And, and when in your mem'ry, my kind vision you'll see,
   Then, then will I know surely, our love eternal will be.

   Ja, ja, ja, ja, our love eternal will be.

Ein Prosit der Gemütlichkeit

Ein Pro - sit, ein Pro - sit der Ge - müt - lich - keit, ein

Pro - sit, ein Pro - sit der Ge - müt - lich - keit!

Trinksprüche

Drinking Song

Hoch soll er le - ben, hoch soll er le - ben, drei - mal hoch!

Er le - be hoch, er le - be hoch! Er le - be hoch, er le - be

hoch, hoch, hoch, hoch, hoch, ja drei - mal hoch!

Im Krug zum grünen Kranze

At the Green Wreath Tavern

1. Im Krug zum grü - nen Kran - ze, da kehrt ich dur - stig ein; da
2. Ein Glas war ein - ge - gos - sen, das wur - de nim - mer leer; sein
3. Ich tät mich zu ihm set - zen, ich sah ihm ins Ge - sicht; das

saß ein Wand - rer drin - nen, ja drin - nen am Tisch beim küh - len Wein, da
Haupt ruht auf dem Bün - del, ja Bün - del, als wär's ihm viel zu schwer, sein
schien mir gar be - freun - det, be - freun - det, und den - noch kannt'ich's nicht, das

saß ein Wand - rer drin - nen, ja drin - nen am Tisch beim küh - len Wein.
Haupt ruht auf dem Bün - del, ja Bün - del, als wär's ihm viel zu schwer.
schien mir gar be - freun - det, be - freun - det, und den - noch kannt'ich's nicht.

4. Da sah auch mir ins Auge
   Der fremde Wandersmann
   Und füllte meinen Becher, ja Becher,
   Und sah mich wieder an.

5. Hei, was die Becher klangen,
   Wie brannte Hand in Hand!
   "Es lebe die Liebste deine, ja deine,
   Herzbruder, im Vaterland!"

1. Once at the Green Wreath Tavern
     I stopped, my thirst to quench,
   A wayfarer was sitting (sitting)
     Beside the tavern bench.

2. His glass was filled before him
     The wine he never drank;
   His head was passing heavy (heavy),
     And on his pack it sank.

3. I sat me down beside him
     And gazed him well, I wot,
   His face seemed right familiar (familiar),
     And yet I knew it not.

4. He too gazed deeply at me,
     This stranger, but in vain;
   And then he filled my goblet (goblet),
     Then looked at me again.

5. 'T was then we clinked our glasses,
     As hand was grasped in hand;
   "A health to her, old fellow (fellow).
     Your dearest in the land!"

In München steht ein Hofbräuhaus

In Munich Stands a Hofbrauhaus

Verse

1. Da, wo die grü - ne I - sar fliesst, wo man mit Grüss Gott' dich grüsst, liegt mei-ne schö-ne

Münch - ner Stadt, die ih-res-gleichen nicht hat. Wasser ist billig, rein und gut, nur ver-

dünnt es un - ser Blut, schöner sind Tropfen gold-nen Wein's, a - ber am schönsten ist eins: In

Refrain

Mün - chen steht ein Hof-bräu - haus, eins zwei g'suffa. Da läuft so man-ches

Fäss-chen aus. eins zwei g'suffa. Da hat schon man - cher bra - ve Mann. eins

zwei g'suf-fa. ge-zeigt, was er so ver-tra-gen kann. Schon früh am Morgen fing er an, und spät am

A - bend kam er her - aus! So schön ist's im Hof - bräu - haus! haus!

Fine

2. Da trinkt man Bier nicht aus dem Glas,
Da gibt's nur die grosse Mass!
Und wenn der erste Masskrug leer.
Bringt dir die Reserl bald mehr.
Oft kriegt zu Haus die Frau ein Schreck.
Bleibt der Mann mal länger weg.
Aber die braven Nachbarsleut.
Die wissen besser Bescheid!

3. Wenn auch so manche deutsche Stadt
Sehenswürdigkeiten hat,
Eins gibt es nirgend wo wie hier.
Das ist das Münchener Bier.
Der dieses kleine Lied erdacht,
Hat so manche lange Nacht
Über dem Münchner Bier studiert
Und hat es gründlich probiert.

1. There where the Isar River flows,
Everyone's kindness clearly shows,
There lies my München, city fair,
No other one can compare.
Water is cheap and clean and good
But it also thins down the blood.
Sipping gold wine so good it is
But best of all drinks is this.

Chorus

In München stands a Hofbrau House
Eins, zwei, prosit.
Where many a keg's been emptied out
Eins, zwei, prosit.
It's there where many a solid man
Eins, zwei, prosit
Has proven how much to consume he can.
In early morning he began
And late at night he reappeared
From fun in the Hofbrau House.

2. Beer is not served in a tiny glass,
Only a full litre mug has class.
And when you've finished with the first,
Soon they'll bring more for the thirst.
Often the wife's concern is strong,
When the husband stays too long.
But the good neighbors keep her calm,
They know there is no great harm.

3. Many a German town we know,
Has a lot of sights to show,
But we find one thing only here,
That is the Münchener beer.
He who composed this little song
Has at times the whole night long
Studied by it to the morning bell,
Tasted and tested it well.

89

Hab' mein' Wage vollgelade

Filled My Wagon

1. Hab' mein' Wa - ge voll - ge - la - de, voll mit al - ten
2. Hab' mein' Wa - ge voll - ge - la - de, voll mit Män - nern
3. Hab' mein' Wa - ge voll - ge - la - de, voll mit jun - gen

Weib - sen. Als wir in die Stadt nein - ka - men, fing'n sie an zu
al - ten. Als wir in die Stadt nein - ka - men, murr-ten sie und
Mäd - chen. Als wir zu dem Tor nein - ka - men, san-gen sie durchs

kei - fen. Drum lad' ich all' mein' Le - be - ta - ge nie
schal - ten. Drum lad' ich all' mein' Le - be - ta - ge nie
Städt - chen. Drum lad' ich all' mein' Le - be - ta - ge nur

al - te Weib-sen auf mein' Wa - ge. Hü, Schim - mel, hü!
al - te Män-ner auf mein' Wa - ge. Hü, Schim - mel, hü!
jun - ge Mäd-chen auf mein' Wa - ge. Hü, Schim - mel, hü!

1. Took my wagon, started loading, with old women, straining
   When we came into the city, they began complaining
   Therefore, I tell you in a hurry,
   No more old women in my surrey.
   Go, horses Go!

2. Took my wagon, started loading it with older menfolk
   When we came into the city, trouble started tenfold
   Therefore, I tell you in a hurry
   No more old menfolk in my surrey.
   Go, horses Go!

3. Took my wagon, started loading with young girls so charming
   When the city gates we entered, they sang songs, heartwarming
   Therefore, I tell you in a hurry,
   Young girls from now on in my surrey.
   Go, horses Go!

Ich bin ein Musikante

I Am a Music Maker

1. Ich bin ein Mu-si-kan-te und komm aus Schwa-ben-land. Wir sind auch Mu-si-kan-ten und komm'n aus Schwa-ben-land.

Einer: Ich kann spie-len Vi-o-vi-o-vi-o-lin.

Alle: Wir kön-nen spie-len Baß, Vi-ol' und Flöt. Und wir kön-nen tan-zen hop-sa-sa, hop-sa-sa, hop-sa-sa und wir kön-nen tan-zen hop-sa-sa, hop-sa-sa.

2. Ich bin ein Musikante.........   Wir sind auch...
Ich kann blasen die Trompete...   Kehrreim: Tengtereng...

I am a music maker
I came from Schwabenland
We all are music makers
We come from Schwabenland
I can play my Vi-o vi-o vi-o-lin
We can play our Bass Vi-ol' and Flute
And we're joyful dancing
Hop-sa-sa, hop-sa-sa
And we're joyful dancing
Hop-sa-sa, hop-sa-sa.

Lustig ist das Zigeunerleben

A Happy Gypsy Life

1. Lu-stig ist das Zi - geu - ner - le - ben, far - ri-a, fa - ri - a,

brauch'n dem Kai-ser kein Zins zu ge - ben, fa - ri - a, fa - ri - a.

Lu - stig ist es im grü - nen Wald, wo des Zi - geu - ners Auf - ent - halt!

Fa - ri - a, fa - ri - a, fa - ri - a, fa - ri - a, fa - ri - a, fa - ri - a.

2. Sollt uns einmal der Hunger plagen,
tun wir uns ein Hirschlein jagen,
Hirschlein, nimm dich wohl in acht,
wenn des Jagers Büchse kracht

3. Sollt uns einmal der Durst sehr quälen,
gehn wir hin zu Waldesquellen,
trinken das Wasser wie Moselwein,
meinen, es müsste Champagner sein

4. Mädel, willst du Tabak rauchen,
brauchst dir keine Pfeif zu kaufen,
Greif in meine Tasch hinein,
da wird Pfeif und Tabak sein

5. Wenn uns tut der Beutel hexen,
lassen wir einen Taler wechseln,
treiben wir die Zigeunerkunst,
habn wir den Taler schon wieder bei uns

6. Wenn wir auch kein Federbett haben,
tun wir uns ein Loch ausgraben,
legen Moos und Reisig 'nein,
das soll uns ein Federbett sein

1. A gypsy's life is free and gay, faria, faria.
No one asks him a tax to pay, faria, faria.
Merry times in the woods they share,
That's the gypsy's life so fair.
Faria, faria, faria, faria, faria, faria.

O du lieber Augustin

Oh, My Dear Old Augustine

O du lie-ber Au-gustin, Au-gustin, Au-gustin, o du lie-ber
Oh my dear old Au-gustin, Au-gustin, Au-gustin, Oh my dear old

Au-gustin, Al-les ist hin! Geld ist weg, Mäd'l ist weg, Al-les weg,
Au-gustin, Everything's gone! Mon-ey's gone, Girl is gone, All is gone,

Al-les weg! O du lie-ber Au-gustin, Al-les ist hin!
All is gone! Oh my dear old Au-gus-tin, Ev-'ry-thing's gone!

93

Trink, Trink, Brüderlein Trink!

Drink, Drink, Come Brother Drink!

1. Wenn
2. Bei

du er-wachst am Mor - gen und schlägst die Au-gen dann auf, be-
Freun-den, Frau'n und Lie - dern be - ru - higst du oft dein Herz, doch

drän - gen dich oft Sor - gen be - ginnst du den Ta - ges - lauf; hilft
kommt der Gram bald wie - der, zu ihm ge-sellt sich der Schmerz. So

sie dir kei - ner tra - gen und kommst du nicht zur Ruh' an
wie sie neu er - schei - nen die Sor - gen, Kum - mer, Pein, fang'

sol - chen schwe-ren Ta - gen ruf ich als Freund dir zu:
nur nicht an zu wei - nen, schenk dir ein Gläs - chen ein:

Chorus: Trink, trink Brü-der-lein trink, lass doch die Sor-gen zu Haus,

Trink, trink, Brü-der-lein trink, trin-ke dein Gläs-chen nur aus;

la-che, lie-be und trin-ke dich satt, nur da-ran Freu-de man hat, flieh' dem

Kum-mer und meide den Schmerz dann ist ja das Leben ein Scherz. Scherz.

D.C.
Fine

1. When you awake at morning and feel that life is a grind;
Just take this timely warning and leave Old Man Gloom behind.
A glass with foam or bubbles will wash your cares away;
It's hard to think of troubles if you do as I say:

2. When friends and luck desert you and life is burdened with woe,
Don't let your worries hurt you, you only live once you know;
Be gay and lift your glass up and once your spirits rise,
You'll find it hard to pass up the cure that I advise:

Chorus: Drink, drink, come brother drink, drink all your troubles away
            Drink, drink, come brother drink, drink or your hair will turn gray,
            Drown your sorrow and banish your care, raising your glass with a song
            Drink, your worries will vanish in air and good luck come rolling along.

95

Vogelhochzeit

Bird's Wedding

Wal - de. Vi-di - ral-la-la, vi-di - ral-la-la, vi-di - ral-la-la-la - la.

2. Die Drossel war der Bräutigam,
die Amsel war die Braute.
Vi-de-ral-la-la, vi-de-ral-la-la,
vi-de-ral-la-la-la-la.

3. Der Sperber, der Sperber,
der war der Hochzeitswerber.
Vi-de-ral-la-la, vi-de-ral-la-la,
vi-de-ral-la-la-la-la.

4. Die Lerche, die Lerche,
die führt die Braut zur Kerche.
Vi-de-ral-la-la, vi-de-ral-la-la,
vi-de-ral-la-la-la-la.

5. Frau Nachtigall, Frau Nachtigall,
die sang mit ihrem schönsten Schall.
Vi-de-ral-la-la, vi-de-ral-la-la,
vi-de-ral-la-la-la-la.

6. Der Spatz, der kocht das Hochzeitsmahl,
verzehrt die schönsten Bissen all.
Vi-de-ral-la-la, vi-de-ral-la-la,
vi-de-ral-la-la-la-la.

7. Die Finken, die Finken,
die brachten was zu trinken.
Vi-de-ral-la-la, vi-de-ral-la-la,
vi-de-ral-la-la-la-la.

8. Die Gänse und die Anten,
das war'n die Musikanten.
Vi-de-ral-la-la, vi-de-ral-la-la,
vi-de-ral-la-la-la-la.

9. Brautmutter war die Eule,
nahm Abschied mit Geheule.
Vi-de-ral-la-la, vi-de-ral-la-la,
vi-de-ral-la-la-la-la.

10. Der Hahn, der krähte "Gute Nacht!"
Da wart die Lampe ausgemacht.
Vi-de-ral-la-la, vi-de-ral-la-la,
vi-de-ral-la-la-la-la.

11. Nun ist die Vogelhochzeit aus,
und alle ziehn vergnügt nach Haus.
Vi-de-ral-la-la-, vi-de-ral-la-la,
vi-de-ral-la-la-la-la.

1. A bird wanted to have a wedding in the lovely green forest.

2. The thrush was the groom and the blackbird the bride.

3. The sparrowhawk was the matchmaker.

4. The lark led the bride to the church.

5. Mrs. Nightingale sang with her loveliest voice.

6. The sparrow cooked the wedding feast, but the best morsels he ate himself.

7. The finches brought the drinks.

8. The geese and the ducks were the musicians.

9. The owl was the mother of the bride, took leave with crying and lamenting.

10. The rooster crowed "Good Night" and the lamps were extinguished.

11. Now the wedding is over, everyone is happy and goes home.

Winter Ade

Winter Good-bye

2. Winter ade! Scheiden tut weh.
   Gerne vergess ich dein,
   kannst immer ferne sein.
   Winter ade! Scheiden tut weh.

3. Winter ade! Scheiden tut weh
   Gehst du nicht bald nach Haus,
   lacht dich der Kuckuck aus.
   Winter ade! Scheiden tut weh.

1. Winter, good-bye! At parting we cry.
   Your leaving does not sting;
   It makes my heart to sing.

2. Winter, good-bye! At parting we cry.
   Gladly forgetting thee,
   You keep away from me.

3. Winter, good-bye! At parting we cry.
   Quickly go, one and two,
   Or cuckoo laughs at you.

Also may be sung as Liebchen, ade

1. Liebchen, ade! Scheiden tut weh.
   Weil ich denn scheiden muss,
   gib mir den letzten Kuss!
   Liebchen, ade! Scheiden tut weh.

2. Liebchen, ade! Scheiden tut weh.
   Wahre der Liebe dein,
   stets will ich treu dir sein!
   Liebchen, ade! Scheiden tut weh.

3. Liebchen ade! Scheiden tut weh.
   Wein nicht die Äuglein rot,
   trennt uns ja selbst kein Tod!
   Liebchen ade! Scheiden tut weh.

1. Sweetheart, good-bye, please do not cry.
   Leaving you hurts my heart,
   Kiss me before we part,
   Sweetheart, good-bye, please do not cry.

2. Sweetheart, good-bye, please do not cry.
   Knowing you're loving me,
   Faithful to you I'll be,
   Sweetheart, good-bye, please do not cry.

3. Sweetheart, good-bye, please do not cry.
   Our love forever is,
   Not even death changes this,
   Sweetheart, good-bye, please do not cry.

Z'Lauterbach

In Lauterbach

2. Z' Lauterbach hab' i mein Herz verlor'n,
   Ohne Herz kann i net leb'n!
   Muss i bald wieder nach Lauterbach,
   's Dirndel soll's seine mir geb'n!

3. 's Dirndel hat schwarzbraune Äugele,
   Nett, wie a Täuberl schaut's her;
   Wann i beim Fenster oan Schnagler tu',
   Kommt se ganz freundlich daher!

1. Lauterbach is where I lost my sock,
   I won't go home without it.
   So I go back then to Lauterbach
   Buy me another to fit.

2. Lauterbach is where I lost my heart,
   Living without, what a task!
   Therefore, I must go to Lauterbach
   My sweetheart for her's I will ask.

3. Dark brown the eyes of my sweetheart are,
   Looks at me, coy, like a dove.
   When by her window I softly call,
   She comes to show me her love.

98

Abendlied
Evening Song

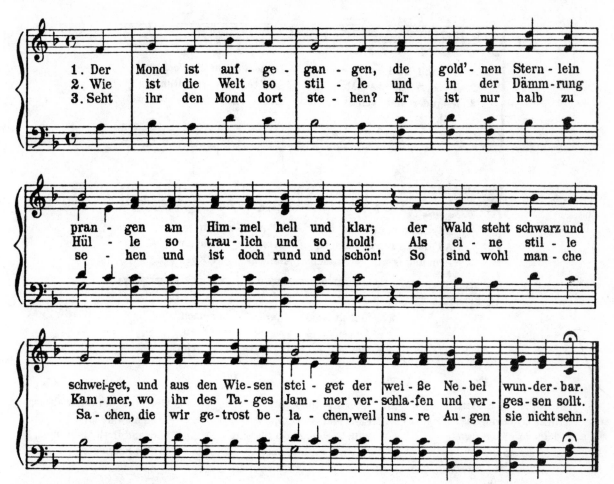

1. Der Mond ist auf-ge-gan-gen, die gold'-nen Stern-lein
2. Wie ist die Welt so stil-le und in der Dämm-rung
3. Seht ihr den Mond dort ste-hen? Er ist nur halb zu

pran-gen am Him-mel hell und klar; der Wald steht schwarz und
Hül-le so trau-lich und so hold! Als ei-ne stil-le
se-hen und ist doch rund und schön! So sind wohl man-che

schwei-get, und aus den Wie-sen stei-get der wei-ße Ne-bel wun-der-bar.
Kam-mer, wo ihr des Ta-ges Jam-mer ver-schla-fen und ver-ges-sen sollt.
Sa-chen, die wir ge-trost be-la-chen,weil uns-re Au-gen sie nicht sehn.

1. The moon so mild and tender,
   The stars in all their splendor
   Light up the evening sky,
   While veils of mist are hovering
   Above the woods and covering
   The meadows as the night goes by.

2. How still the world is resting,
   And in the twilight nesting
   As in a shelter warm;
   Where you may fear no sorrow,
   And what might come tomorrow,
   Forget and safely sleep till morn.

3. You see the moon rise slowly,
   Showing but half so lowly,
   Yet it is round and bright.
   So many a thing is like that
   Which carelessly we laugh at
   Because it's hidden from our sight.

Abend wird es wieder

Now the Day is Over

1. A - bend wird es wie - der, Lei - se kommt die Nacht;
2. Je - su, gib den Mü - den Sanf - te, sü - sse Ruh';
3. Wenn der Mor - gen däm - mert, Lass mich froh aufsteh'n

An dem Him - mel fun - kelt Gold'ne Sternenpracht.
All' die nas - sen Au - gen Schliesse seg - nend zu.
Rein und frisch und sündlos An mein Tagwerk geh'n.

funkelt Gold'ne Ster - - - nenpracht.
Au - gen Schliesse seg - - - nend zu.
Sündlos An mein Tagwerk geh'n.

1. Now the day is over,
   Night is drawing nigh,
   Shadows of the evening
   Steal across the sky.

2. Jesus give the weary,
   Calm and sweet repose
   With Thy tend'rest blessing
   May our eyelids close.

3. When the morning wakens,
   Then may we arise
   Pure and fresh and sinless,
   In Thy holy eyes.

Alle Vögel sind schon da

All the Birds Returned Again

1. Al - le Vö - gel sind schon da, al - le Vö - gel, al - le!
2. Wie sie al - le lu - stig sind, flink und froh sich re - gen!
3. Was sie uns ver - kün - det nun, neh - men wir zu Her - zen:

Welch ein Sin - gen, Mu - si - zier'n, Pfei - fen, Zwit-schern, Ti - ri - lier'n!
Am - sel, Dros - sel, Fink und Star und die gan - ze Vo - gel-schar
wir auch wol - len lu - stig sein, lu - stig wie die Vö - ge - lein,

Früh - ling will nun ein - marschier'n, kommt mit Sang und Schal - le.
wün - schen dir ein fro - hes Jahr, lau - ter Heil und Se - gen.
hier und dort, feld - aus, feld - ein, sin - gen, sprin-gen, scher - zen!

1. All the birds returned again,
   Chasing winter sadness,
   Making music great and small
   Chirping, trilling, singing all
   Springtime can't be far at all
   Comes with song and gladness.

2. Joyfully they flit about,
   Their songs our ears caressing.
   Blackbirds, starlings, finches dear
   All the birds with one big cheer
   Wishing us a happy year
   Filled with endless blessing.

3. Listen to their message now
   They to us are bringing.
   Happy is their life and free
   As they are, we want to be
   Here and there so merrily
   Spreading joy and singing.

An den Mai

In May

1. Komm, lie - ber Mai, und ma - che die Bäu - me wie - der grün, und laß uns an dem Ba - che die klei - nen Veil - chen blühn! Wie möch - ten wir so ger - ne ein Blüm-chen wie - der sehn, ach lie - ber Mai, wie ger - ne ein - mal spa - zie - ren gehn!

2. Zwar Win - ter - ta - ge ha - ben wohl auch der Freu - den viel! Man kann im Schnee eins tra - ben und treibt manch A - bend-spiel, baut Häu - ser-chen von Kar - ten, spielt Blin - de-kuh und Pfand, auch gibt's wohl Schlit-ten - fahr - ten auf's lie - be, frei - e Land.

3. Doch wenn die Vög-lein sin - gen und wir dann froh und flink auf grü - nem Ra - sen sprin - gen, das ist ein an - der Ding! Drum komm und bring vor al - len uns vie - le Veil - chen mit, bring auch viel Nach - ti - gal - len und schö - ne Kuk - kucks mit!

Synopsis:

1. Come, lovely May, delight us
   with leaves on every tree,
   and violets by the river
   for our eyes to see.
   We yearn to see the flowers
   come sprouting from the ground,
   Oh lovely May, and sunshine
   to leisurely walk around.

2. Winter days are fun too.
   You can play all kinds of
   indoor games or play in the snow
   and take a sleigh ride across the land.

3. But when the birds are singing, and
   we can skip and run on the fresh green
   grass, that is altogether different.
   So come (May) and bring us violets,
   nightingales and cuckoos.

102

Das stille Tal

The Quiet Valley

1. Im schön-sten Wie-sen-grun-de ist mei-ner Hei-mat Haus, da
2. Müßt' aus dem Tal ich schei-den, wo al-les Lust und Klang; das
3. Sterb' ich, in Ta-les Grun-de will ich be-gra-ben sein, singt

zog ich man-che Stun-de ins Tal hin-aus. Dich, mein stil-les Tal, grüß' ich
wär mein herb-stes Lei-den, mein letz-ter Gang. Dich, mein stil-les Tal, grüß' ich
mir zur letz-ten Stun-de beim A-bend-schein: „Dir, o stil-les Tal, Gruß zum

tau-send mal! Da zog ich man-che Stun-de ins Tal hin-aus.
tau-send mal! Das wär mein herb-stes Lei-den, mein letz-ter Gang.
letz-ten mal!" Singt mir zur letz-ten Stun-de beim A-bend-schein.

1. Amidst the valley's flowers
There stands my father's home,
Where I for many hours
Found room to roam.
Peaceful valley mine,
All my love is thine;
Where I for many hours
Found room to roam.

2. If I one day must leave here
Where all is happiness,
Would be my greatest sorrow,
My last distress.
Peaceful valley mine,
All my love is thine;
Would be my greatest sorrow,
My last distress.

3. And if I die, oh bury me
At this beloved site;
And sing at my last hour
By evening light;
Peaceful valley mine,
All my love is thine;
This sing at my last hour
By evening light.

Rätsel.

Wer ist so klug, wer ist so schlau?
Dem schüttl' ich was vom Bäumchen!
's ist innen gelb und außen blau,
hat mitten drin ein Steinchen.

(Die Pflaume)

103

Das Wandern

The Wandering

4. |: Die Steine selbst, so schwer sie sind, :|
Die Steine!
Sie tanzen mit den muntern Reihn
|: Und wollen gar noch schneller sein, :|
|: Die Steine! :|

5. |: O Wandern, Wandern, meine Lust, :|
O Wandern!
Herr Meister und Frau Meisterin,
|: Laßt mich im Frieden weiter ziehn :|
|: Und wandern! :|

1. The wandering is the miller's joy,
   The wandering is the miller's joy, the wandering.
   A miller master he is not,
   If wandering never crossed his thought,
   If wandering never crossed his thought,
   ||: The wandering, :||

2. We learned it from the waters swift,
   We learned it from the waters swift, the waters.
   Forever moving night and day,
   Their wandering is the only way,
   Their wandering is the only way,
   ||: The waters, :||

3. The wheels are shoving us to move,
   The wheels are shoving us to move, the wheels.
   They keep on turning, freely turn,
   From their persistence we can learn,
   From their persistence we can learn,
   ||: The wheels, :||

4. The boulders, heavy as they are,
   The boulders, heavy as they are, the boulders.
   Are dancing, twirling merrily,
   Yet faster still they want to be,
   Yet faster still they want to be,
   ||: The boulders, :||

5. My joy in life is wandering,
   My joy in life is wandering, is wandering.
   Dear master and dear master's wife,
   Let wandering be my lot in life,
   Let wandering be my lot in life,
   ||: Keep wandering, :||

O wie wohl ist mir am Abend

O How Lovely is the Evening

O how lovely is the evening, is the evening,
When the bells are sweetly ringing, sweetly ringing,
Ding, dong, ding, dong, ding, dong.

Der Wirtin Töchterlein

The Inkeeper's Daughter

2. "Mein Bier und Wein ist frisch und klar,
    ‖: Mein Töchterlien liegt auf der Totenbahr'," :‖
    Und als sie traten zur Kammer hinein,
    ‖: Da lag sie in einem schwarzen Schrein. :‖

3. Der erste schlug den Schleier zurück,
    ‖: Und schaute sie an mit traurigem Blick, :‖
    "Ach, lebtest du noch, du schöne Magd,
    ‖: Ich würde dich lieben von dieser Zeit." :‖

4. Der zweite deckte den Schleier zu,
    ‖: Und kehrte sich ab und weinte dazu, :‖
    "Ach, dass du liegst auf der Totenbahr',
    ‖: Ich hab' dich geliebet so manches Jahr." :‖

5. Der dritte hub ihn wieder sogleich,
    ‖: Und küsste sie an den Mund so bleich: :‖
    Dich liebt' ich immer, dich lieb' ich noch heut',
    ‖: "Und werde dich lieben in Ewigheit." :‖

1.   Three jolly good fellows came over the Rhine,
    ‖: And there they turned in at a tavern to dine:‖
    "Ho! Mistress, how goes it for ale and wine?
    ‖: And where is that pretty wench of thine?":‖

2.   "My wine is good, my ale is clear,
    ‖: My daughter is lying upon her bier.":‖
    Then to the chamber she led them back,
    ‖: And there she lay in her coffin black,:‖

3.   The first one he threw the shroud aside,
    ‖: And said, as he gazed at her sad-eyed,:‖
    "My beauty, and wert thou not dead and gone,
    ‖: I swear I should love thee, from this day on.":‖

4.   The second he covered the maiden's face,
    ‖: And turned him away, and wept a space:‖
    "That thou art lying upon thy bier,
    ‖: When I have so loved thee, this many a year!":‖

5.   The third again threw off her the veil,
    ‖: And kissed her lips that were dead and pale:‖
    "I always loved thee, I love thee still;
    ‖: For ever and ever, I always will.":‖

Das Lied vom feinen Mädchen.

Ich bin ein feines Mädchen,
kann drehen das Rädchen,
kann flicken und stricken
und putzen und stutzen;
kann nädeln und fädeln,
kann singen und springen
und braten und kochen
das Fleisch und die Knochen.

Der Lindenbaum

The Linden Tree

1. Beyond the city gateway
    There stands a linden-tree,
And often in its shadow
    Sweet dreams have come to me;
Its bark I have engraven
    With many a loving name,
For aye in love or longing
    T'was there I always came

2. To-day I had to pass it,
    'T was very late at night,
And even in the darkness
    I shut my eyelids tight;
I heard its branches rustle
    These words to me addressed:
"Come here to me, old comrade,
    Come here and be at rest!"

3. The wind was cold and bitter,
    And blowing in my face,
Away my hat went soaring,
    I didn't give it chase.
Now, though they are behind me
    Full many a weary mile,
I hear the branches rustle:
    "Come here and rest awhile."

Die alte Heimat war zu enge

The Old Homeland was too Confining

1. Die al - te Heim - at war zu eng - e Es fehlt das täg - lich Brot im

Haus   Da grif - fen viel - e zu dem Sta - be Und zo - gen flugs und fröh - lich aus.

2. Die goldne Morgensonne lockte,
   Ihr heller Glanz war gar zu schön!
   Ihr ging man unbeirrt entgegen
   Und Wollt den schönen Osten sehn.

3. Die ew'ge Freiheit ist zu Ende,
   Die Katharina ihnen bot.
   Das Wandern, Wandern nimmt kein Ende!
   Wohin? Das weiss allein nur Gott.

4. Es kamen von dem Volga Strome
   Nun viele auch in unser Land
   Mit neuem, starkem Gottvertrauen
   Ein guter, alter Bauernstand.

5. Die helle, helle Sonne leuchtet
   Uns stets und warm mit eigner Pracht.
   Das Herz erfreut sich täglich wieder
   An dem, was Gott für uns gemacht.

6. Wir preisen ihn von ganzem Herzen
   Und danken danken, ihm dafür.
   Mög' er dies schöne Land bewahren
   Und segnen, segnen für und für!

1. When the old homeland was confining
   And scarce became the daily bread,
   Many decided to forsake it
   And journey far away instead.

2. The golden morning sun was beckoning,
   Its brilliant ray like a command,
   And unperturbed they went to meet it,
   Wanted to see the eastern land.

3. The lasting freedom now has ended
   Which Empress Catherine promised those.
   Pack up once more and journey farther!
   Which way to turn? God only knows.

4. Already from the Volga River
   Many have come to our land,
   Trusting in God, in faith abiding,
   Straightforth the mind and strong the hand.

5. The sun with all its gracious splendor
   Is shining still and warming us.
   Our heart rejoices every morning
   For God provides and cares for us.

6. For this we praise him and we thank him,
   With grateful hearts we him adore.
   May he protect this land of ours
   And bless it, bless it evermore.

Die Gedanken sind frei

The Thoughts are Free

1. Die Ge - dan - ken sind frei! Wer kann sie er - ra - ten? Sie flie - hen vor -bei wie nächt - li - che Schat - ten. Kein Mensch kann sie wis - sen, kein Jä - ger er - schie - ssen, es blei - bet da - bei: Die Ge - dan - ken sind frei!

2. Ich denke, was ich will
und was mich beglücket,
doch alles in der Still,
und wie es sich schicket.
Mein Wunsch und Begehren
kann niemand verwehren,
es bleibet dabei:
Die Gedanken sind frei!

3. Und sperrt man mich ein
in finsteren Kerker,
das alles sind rein
vergebliche Werke;
denn meine Gedanken
zerreissen die Schranken
und Mauern entzwei:
Die Gedanken sind frei!

4. Drum will ich auf immer
den Sorgen entsagen,
und will mich auch nimmer
mit Grillen mehr plagen.
Man kann ja im Herzen
stets lachen und scherzen
und denken dabei:
Die Gedanken sind frei!

1. The thoughts are always free,
Who's able to guess them?
Away from us they flee.
No one else may possess them.
No person can know them.
No hunter can shoot them.
It always will be
That our thoughts shall be free.

2. I think then what I want
And what does delight me,
With proper restraint
And always so quietly.
My wish and desire
Can no one deny me.
It always will be
That our thoughts shall be free.

Die Lorelei

The Lorelei

Fr. Silcher

1. Ich weiss nicht, was soll es be - deu - ten, dass ich so trau-rig bin? Ein
2. Die schön - ste Jung-frau sit - zet dort o - ben wun-der - bar, ihr
3. Den Schif-fer im klei - nen Schif - fe er-greift es mit wil-dem Weh, er

Mär - chen aus al - ten Zei - ten, das kommt mir nicht aus dem Sinn. Die
gold - nes Ge-schmeide blit - zet, sie kämmt ihr gol - de-nes Haar. Sie
schaut nicht die Fel - sen-rif - fe, er schaut nur hin-auf in die Höh'. Ich

Luft ist kühl und es dun - kelt und ru - hig fliesst der Rhein; der
kämmt es mit gol - de-nem Kam - me und singt ein Lied da - bei; das
glau - be, die Wel-len ver-schlin - gen am En - de Schiffer und Kahn, und

Gi - pfel des Ber - ges fun - kelt im A - bend-son-nen - schein.
hat ei - ne wun-der - sa - me, ge - wal - ti-ge Me - lo - dei.
das hat mit ih - rem Sin - gen die Lo - re-ley ge - tan.

1. I cannot discover the reason
     I feel so sad today,
   Some myth of the earliest ages,
     I cannot drive it away.
   The air is cool, it is evening,
     The Rhine flows slowly by,
   The peak of the mountain glitters
     Against the evening sky.

2. A fair and wondrous maiden
     Is sitting over there,
   Her golden jewels are flashing,
     She combs her golden hair.
   She combs with a comb that is golden,
     And all the while she sings
   A song that is power and wonder
     And all mysterious things.

3. The fisherman there in his shallop
     Is filled with a wild delight,
   He marks not the rocks that are round him,
     He looks but aloft to the height.
   I fancy that boat and boatman
     The waves at last have caught,
   And this with her wondrous singing
     The Lorelei has wrought.

111

Doktor Eisenbart

Doctor Ironbeard

1. Ich bin der Doktor Ei-senbart, val-le-ral-le-ri, juch - hei! ku - rier' die Leut'nach mei-ner Art, val-le-ral-le-ri, juch - hei! kann ma-chen, dass die Blin-den geh'n, valle-ralle-ri, juch - heiras-sa! und dass die Lahmen wieder seh'n! Valle-ralle-ri, juch - hei!

2. Zu Ulm kuriert' ich einen Mann,
Dass ihm das Blut vom Beine rann:
Er wollte gern gekuhpockt sein,
Ich impft's ihm mit dem Bratspiess ein.

3. Des Küster's Sohn in Dideldum,
Dem gab ich zehn Pfund Opium:
Drauf schlief er Jahre, Tag und Nacht,
Und ist bis jetzt noch nicht erwacht.

4. Es hatt' ein Mann in Langensalz
Ein'n zentnerschweren Kropf am Hals:
Den schnürt' ich mit dem Hellseil zu,
Probatum est, er hat jetzt Ruh'!

5. Zu Prag, da nahm ich einem Weib
Zehn Fuder Steine aus dem Leib;
Der letzte war ihr Leichenstein:
Sie wird wohl jetzt kurieret sein.

6. Das ist die Art, wie ich kurier',
Sie ist probat, ich bürg' dafür;
Dass jedes Mittel Wirkung tut,
Schwör'ich bei meinem Doktorhut.

1. My name is Doctor Ironbeard
Valleralleri, hurrah!
To cure the folks I am prepared;
Valleralleri, hurrah!
'T is I that make the dumb to walk,
Valleralleri, hurrah, hurrah!
And I can make the lame to talk!
Valleralleri, hurrah!

2. At Ulm a certain man did beg
Me to inoculate his leg,
I caused the blood to flow from it
By vaccination with the spit.

3. The sexton's son in Didledum
I dosed a pound of opium;
He slept some years, both day and night,
And he is sleeping yet, all right.

4. A man in Langensalz' I found,
Whose goiter weighed a hundred pound,
A brake chain tied it up for me,
And now he's happy — Q.E.D.

5. In Prague I took from one old crone
A good ten wagonload of stone;
Her gravestone was the last I found:
She's cured for good, now, I'll be bound.

6. And that's the way the folks I cure,
And I'll go bail the way is sure;
Each remedy's as sure as fate.
I'll swear it by my Doctorate!

Edelweiss

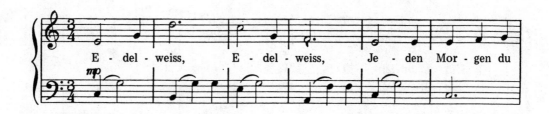

E - del - weiss, E - del - weiss, Je - den Mor - gen du

grüsst mich. Schön und klein, weiss und rein,

Siehst du mich, bist du glück - lich. Blü - te von Schnee, mögst du

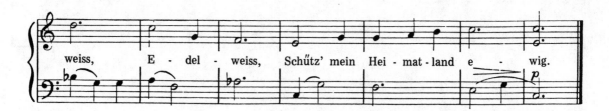

stets ge - deihn, Stets ge - deihn zum Se - gen. E - del -

weiss, E - del - weiss, Schütz' mein Hei - mat - land e - wig.

Edelweiss, Edelweiss,
Every morning you greet me.
Small and white, Clean and bright,
You look happy to meet me.
Blossom of snow, may you bloom and grow,
bloom and grow forever.
Edelweiss, Edelweiss,
Bless my homeland forever.

Ein Männlein steht im Walde

The Little Man in the Forest

1. Ein Männ-lein steht im Wal - de ganz still und stumm; es
2. Das Männ-lein steht im Wal - de auf ei - nem Bein und

hat von lau - ter Pur - pur ein Mänt - lein um.
hat auf sei - nem Haup - te schwarz Käpp - lein klein.

Sag', wer mag das Männ-lein sein, das da steht im Wald al - lein
Sag', wer mag das Männ-lein sein, das da steht im Wald al - lein

mit dem pur-pur - ro - ten Män - te - lein?
mit dem klei - nen schwar - zen Käp - pe - lein?

Synopsis:

1. On the edge of the forest stands
   a little man wearing a red coat.
   Tell me, who could this little man be?

2. The little man is standing on one leg.
   On his head is a little black cap.
   Tell me, who could this little man be?

(Answer: The rose hip.)

114

Es ritten drei Reiter

The Three Horsemen

1. Three horsemen went riding all out of the town,
    Adieu!
A lass from the window above looked down;
    Adieu!
And if it is parted that we must be,
Then give you your little gold ring to me.
    Adieu, adieu, again!
This starting and parting are pain.

2. The one that doth part us is Death, I trow,
    Adieu!
And many red lips has he parted, ere now,
    Adieu!
He's parted full many a man and wife,
Who might have lived happily all their life
    Adieu, adieu, again!
This starting and parting are pain.

3. He'll part you the child from its cradle, 't is said,
    Adieu!
Now when shall I find me my nut-brown maid?
    Adieu!
And if not tomorrow, then be it today,
'T will make us both happy, and come when it may.
    Adieu, adieu, again!
This starting and parting are pain.

Freut euch des Lebens

Life Let Us Cherish

1-7. Freut euch des Le-bens, weil noch das Lämpchen glüht; pflücket die Ro- se, eh' sie ver- blüht!

Fine.

1. Man schafft so gern sich Sorg' und Müh', sucht Dor-nen auf und fin-det sie, und lässt das Veilchen un- bemerkt, das uns am We - ge blüht.

D. C. al Fine.

2. Wenn scheu die Schöpfung sich verhüllt
   Und laut der Donner ob uns brüllt,
   So lacht am Abend nach dem Sturm
   Die Sonn' uns doppelt schön!

3. Wer Neid und Missgunst sorgsam flieht
   Und G'nügsamkeit im Gärtchen zieht,
   Dem schiesst sie schnell zum Bäumchen auf,
   Das gold'ne Früchte trägt.

4. Wer Redlichkeit und Treue liebt
   Und gern dem ärmern Bruder giebt,
   Bei dem baut sich Zufriedenheit
   So gern ihr Hüttchen auf.

5. Und wenn der Pfad sich furchtbar engt
   Und Missgeschick uns plagt und drängt,
   So reicht die Freundschaft schwesterlich
   Dem Redlichen die Hand.

6. Sie trocknet ihm die Tränen ab
   Und streut ihm Blumen bis ans Grab;
   Sie wandelt Nacht in Dämmerung
   Und Dämmerung in Licht.

7. Sie ist des Lebens schönstes Band.
   Schlingt, Brüder, traulich Hand in Hand!
   So wallt man froh, so wallt man leicht
   In's bessre Vaterland!

Chorus: (Repeat before each verse)

Life let us cherish,
While yet the lamp's aglow;
Gather ye roses,
While yet they blow!

1. We borrow trouble, that we do,
   And hunt for thorns, and find them, too,
   And miss the lovely violet
   That grows beside the way.

2. When tempests all the world enshroud,
   And round us thunders roar aloud,
   At evening when the storm is past
   The sun will smile again.

3. On envious wishes be not bent,
   But in your garden plant Content,
   You'll find it soon becomes a tree,
   That bears you golden fruit.

4. For he who honest lives, and true,
   And helps his poorer neighbor, too,
   Will shortly find that Happiness
   Has come with him to dwell.

5. And when your road grows rough and steep,
   And luck is hard, and sorrow deep,
   The honest man will always find
   A friendly hand to grasp.

6. 'T is Friendship wipes away the tear,
   And drops a flower upon your bier,
   And turns the twilight into dawn,
   And turns the dawn to day.

7. No tie in all the world's so fine!
   Come, brother! Grip your hand in mine,
   And right and free, and hand in hand,
   We'll see the promised land.

Es klappert die Mühle

The Wheel at the Millpond

Es klappert die Mühle am rauschenden Bach, klipp, klapp! Bei Tag und bei Nacht ist der Müller stets wach, klipp, klapp! Er mahlet uns Korn zu dem kräftigen Brot und haben wir dieses, so hat's keine Not. Klipp, klapp! klipp, klapp! klipp, klapp!

The wheel at the mill pond goes merrily round, Clip clop!
The miller sings songs to that comforting sound, Clip clop!
In the still of the night and the heat of the day,
He's grinding his flour and he's singing away,
Clip clop! Clip clop! Clip clop!

117

Frohe Botschaft

Joyful Message

1. Kommt a Vo-gerl ge-flo-gen, setzt sich nied'r auf mein' Strauß-ring zum Fuß, hat a Zet-terl im Go-scherl und vom Di-arndl an Gruß.)
2. Und a Büch-serl zum Schie-ßen und a Di-arndl zum Schlag'n, und a Di-arndl zum Lie-ben muß a lust'-ger Bue han.
3. Hast mi all-weil ver-trö-stet uf die Sum-me-ri-zeit, und der Sum-mer is kum-ma, und mein Schat-zerl is weit.

Dui dui-de dui dui-de dui di-ri di-ri du-li-e.

4. Daheim is mein Schatzerl,
In der Fremd' bin i hier;
Und es fragt halt kein Katzerl,
Kein Hunderl nach mir.
Dui duide dui duide
Dui diri diri dulie.

5. Liebes Vogerl, flieg' weiter
Nimm an Gruss mit, an Kuss!
Und i kann di net b'gleita,
Weil i hierbleiba muss.
Dui duide dui duide
Dui diri diri dulie.

1. Here's a birdie come flying,
And alights on my knee,
With a notelet in 'ts throatlet
From my sweetheart to me.

3. I've been longing all winter
For the summer to come,
And the summer is come now,
But I'm still far from home.

2. To a gun to go shooting,
To a cudgel to fight,
To a lass to make love to,
Every lad has a right.

4. For my sweetheart's at home there,
Here am I far away,
Not a pussy nor a doggy
That will bid me good day.

5. Fly along now, nice birdie,
Take a kiss to my dear,
But I can't go 'long with you
For I've got to stay here!

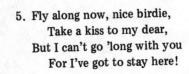

Gelübde

Pledge

1. Ich hab' mich er - ge - ben mit Herz und mit Hand, dir,
2. Mein Herz ist ent - glom - men, dir treu zu - ge - wandt, du
3. Will hal - ten und glau - ben an Gott fromm und frei; will,

Land voll Lieb' und Le - ben, mein teu - res Va - ter - land, dir,
Land der Frei'n und From - men, du herr - lich Va - ter - land, du
Va - ter - land, dir blei - ben auf e - wig fest und treu, will,

Land voll Lieb' und Le - ben, mein teu - res Va - ter - land!
Land der Frei'n und From - men, du herr - lich Va - ter - land!
Va - ter - land, dir blei - ben auf e - wig fest und treu!

1. I pledge my allegiance with heart and with hand
to you above all others, my dearest Fatherland. :‖

2. My heart is aflame for you like a dear friend,
land of the free and faithful, my glorious Fatherland. :‖

3. My trust and obedience to God I will give
and to you my allegiance as long as I shall live. :‖

4. O God hear my promise and lift my young heart,
to a life of faith and freedom and joy set it apart. :‖

119

Heidenröslein

Wild Rose

1. Sah ein Knab ein Rös-lein stehn, Rös-lein auf der Hei-den;
2. Kna-be sprach: ich bre-che dich, Rös-lein auf der Hei-den;
3. Und der wil-de Kna-be brach s'Rös-lein auf der Hei-den;

war so jung und mor-gen-schön, lief er schnell es nah zu sehn, sah's mit vie-len
s'Rös-lein sprach: ich ste-che dich, daß du e-wig denkst an mich und ich will's nicht
s'Rös-lein wehr-te sich und stach, half ihm doch kein Weh und Ach, mußt es e-ben

Freu-den.
lei-den.
lei-den.

Rös-lein, Rös-lein, Rös-lein rot, Rös-lein auf der Hei-den.

1. Of a rose a boy caught sight,
   Rosebud in the heather,
   Young and fair as morning bright;
   Ah! he saw it with delight,
   Quickly ran he thither.
   Rosebud, rosebud, rosebud red,
   Rosebud in the heather.

2. Cries he, "I'm for picking thee,
   Rosebud in the heather!"
   Cries she, "I'm for pricking thee,
   So that thou 'lt remember me!
   I'll not have it, either!"
   Rosebud, rosebud, rosebud red,
   Rosebud in the heather.

3. So the heedless youngster picked
   Rosebud in the heather;
   Flew to arms the rose and pricked,
   Small the pain she could inflict,
   Useless altogether.
   Rosebud, rosebud, rosebud red,
   Rosebud in the heather.

120

Heimatlied der Bessarabiendeutschen

Song of the Bessarabiens' Homeland

1. Gott seg - ne dich, mein Hei-mat-land, ich grüß' dich tausend - mal, dich Land, wo mei-ne
2. So schir - me, Gott, in Freud und Leid du un - ser Heimat -land. Be - wach der Fel-der

Wie - ge stand durch mei - ner Vä - ter Wahl! Du Land, an al - lem Gut so reich, ins
Frucht-bar-keit bis hin zum Schwarzmeerstrand. Er - hal - te du uns deutsch und rein, send

Herz schloß ich dich ein. Ich bleib dir in der Lie - be treu, im To-de bin ich dein!
uns ein freundlich Los, bis wir bei un-sern Vä-tern ruhn, im hei-mat - li-chen Schoß!

1. God bless you, oh my homeland dear,
   I hold you ever close
   O land in which my cradle stood
   'Twas you, my father chose.
   O land so still and beautiful,
   Your love is in my heart.
   I promise you my faithfulness
   Until death may us part.

2. Protect, oh God, in joy and pain
   Our land forevermore.
   Guard fertile fields across the plain
   Up to the Black Sea shore.
   Keep our hearts pure German
   And grant us happy toil
   Until from all our work we rest
   In our own native soil.

121

Heimat
Homeland

1. Die Win - de rau - schen, die Wol - ken ziehn, o fra - get sie
2. Die Blüm-lein er - wa - chen, der Lenz ist nah, o sa - get ihm
3. Auch Vög - lein kom - men von nah und fern, sie kom-men und

nim - mer: wo - hin? wo - hin? denn Wol - ken und Win - de sie
nim - mer: bleib da! bleib da! denn wei - ter er - schlie-ßet der
ge - hen so gern! so gern! und im - mer be - glei - tet sie

denn Wol - ken und
denn wei - ter er -
und im - mer be -

ha - ben kein Herz, sie rau-schen vor - ü - ber ohn' Freu - de und
Him - mel sein Zelt, der Früh-ling muß wan-dern, muß ziehn durch die
ju - beln-der Schall, sie prei - sen den Schöp - fer, er wohnt ü - ber -

Schmerz, sie rau schen vor - ü - ber ohn' Freu - de und Schmerz.
Welt,— der Früh - ling muß wan - dern, muß ziehn durch die Welt.
all,— sie prei - sen den Schöp - fer, er wohnt ü - ber - all.

4. Nur du mein Herz, schaust sehnsuchtsvoll um? o fra - get es nim - mer: wa-

1. The winds are rushing and clouds drift by,
   Yet no one may ask them to where and why?
   For neither the clouds nor the winds have a heart,
   Nor sorrow, nor joy, have no ending, no start.

2. The flowers are waking and spring is here,
   But don't ever tell it: stay here, stay here!
   For wide is the firmament's canopy blue
   And springtime must wander and pass the world through.

3. And birds are coming from far and near,
   Are coming and going, some there, some here!
   Surrounded with joy and with songs in the air,
   They praise their Creator, he lives everywhere.

4. But you, my heart, do longingly sigh?
   Yet no one may ask it: oh why, oh why?
   Who never has felt it will ne'er understand,
   My heart seeks my homeland, my beautiful homeland,
   My heart seeks my homeland, my beautiful homeland,
   My heart seeks my homeland, my heart seeks my homeland,
   My beautiful homeland, my homeland, my beautiful homeland!

Heimliche Liebe

Secret Love

1. Kein Feu - er, kei - ne Koh - le kann bren - nen so heiß als heim - li - che Lie - be, von der nie - mand nichts weiß, von der nie - mand nichts weiß.

2. Keine Rose, keine Nelke kann blühen so schön,
Als wenn zwei verliebte Seelen beieinander tun stehn.

3. Setze du mir einen Spiegel ins Herze hinein,
Damit du kannst sehen, wie so treu ich es mein.

1. No fires, no embers can create more heat
   Than love held in secret, a secret so sweet.

2. No roses or violets under heaven above
   Bloom brighter and sweeter than two hearts in love.

3. Plant within me a mirror so that you may see
   That down in my heart's depth I faithful will be.

Hi lee, hi lo

Hi lee, hi lo, hi lee, hi lo, bei uns gehts im-mer je länger je
schlimmer, hi lee, hi lo, hi lee hi lo, bei uns gehts im-mer noch so.

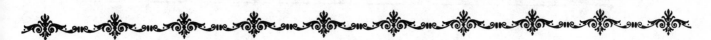

Nach Sibirien muss ich reisen

To Siberia I Must Go

Nach Si-bi-ri-en muss ich jetzt rei-sen, muss ver-las-sen die blü-hen-de Welt
Schwer be-la-den mit skla-vi schem Eisen, har-ret mei-ner nur E-lend und Kält.

O Si-bi-rien, du eis-kal-te Zo-ne, wo kein Schif-fer die Flu-ten durch zieht,

wo kein Fun-ken der Menschheit mehr woh net und das Aug kei-ne Ret-tung mehr sieht.

To Siberia I now must journey,
Leaving behind the flowing world.
Heavily burdened with slavish chains,
I expect only misery and cold.
O Siberia, you icy domain,
Where no zephyr gladdens the meadows,
Where no spark of humanity glows,
And the eye sees no salvation.

Horch, was kommt von draussen rein?

Footsteps by the Door I Hear

4. Wenn mein Liebchen Hochzeit hat,
Hollahi! Hollaho!
Hab ich meinen Trauertag,
Hollahiaho!
Geh dann in mein Kämmerlein,
Hollahi! Hollaho!
Trage meinen Schmerz allein.
Hollahiaho!

5. Wenn ich dann gestorben bin,
Hollahi! Hollaho!
Trägt man mich zum Grabe hin,
Hollahiaho!
Setzt mir keinen Leichenstein,
Hollahi! Hollaho!
Planzt nicht drauf Vergissnichtmein!
Hollahiaho!

1. Footsteps by the door I hear,
   Hol-la-hi! Hol-la-ho!
   Must be my true love, I fear,
   Hol-la-hi-a-ho!
   Passes by, does not look in,
   Hol-la-hi! Hol-la-ho!
   Someone else it must have been.
   Hol-la-hi-a-ho!

2. People often whisper here,
   Hol-la-hi! Hol-la-ho!
   That I have a sweetheart dear,
   Hol-la-hi-a-ho!
   Let them talk, I just keep still
   Hol-la-hi! Hol-la-ho!
   I can love whom love I will.
   Hol-la-hi-a-ho!

3. Tell me, people, to be sure,
   Hol-la-hi! Hol-la-ho!
   What kind of love I must endure,
   Hol-la-hi-a-ho!
   I can't have of whom I'm fond
   Hol-al-hi! Hol-la-ho!
   And another I don't want.
   Hol-la-hi-a-ho!

4. On my sweetheart's wedding day,
   Hol-la-hi! Hol-la-ho!
   Is for me a mourning day,
   Hol-la-hi-a-ho!
   In my room with none to share,
   Hol-la-hi! Hol-la-ho!
   Quietly my pain I bear.
   Hol-la-hi-a-ho!

5. When at last my bell has tolled,
   Ho-la-hi! Hol-la-ho!
   Put me in a grave so cold.
   Hol-la-hi-a-ho!
   No one's there to mark the spot
   Hol-la-hi! Hol-la-ho!
   Or to plant Forget-me-nots.
   Hol-la-hi-a-ho!

Wahre Freundschaft

True Friendship

1. True friendship shall not waver
   Although distance may separate friends;
   Living on in thought and fervor,
   On their faithfulness always depends.

2. My thoughts are always with you,
   Every heartbeat that I am awake!
   I will care for you forever
   Be it morning or midnight late.

3. When vines grow from the millstone
   And bring forth cool wine for you,
   Or when death will take my soul and bone,
   Only then will I cease to be true.

127

Im Schwarzwälder Tal

The Black Forest Vale

1. Es steht ei - ne Müh - le im Schwarzwäl - der Tal, die
2. Und in die - ser Müh - le im Schwarzwäl - der Tal, da
3. Wir reich - ten zum Ab - schied noch ein - mal die Hand und

klap-pert so herr-lich, so schön. Und wo ich geh und
woh-net ein Mä-del so schön. Und wo ich geh und
wünschten ein - an-der viel Glück. Und wo ich geh und

steh im Tal und auf der Höh, da liegt mir die Müh - le, die
steh im Tal und auf der Höh, da liegt mir das Mä - del, das
steh im Tal und auf der Höh, da liegt mir der Abschied, der

Müh - le im Sinn, die Müh - le vom Schwarzwälder Tal.
Mä - del im Sinn, das Mä - del vom Schwarzwälder Tal.
Ab - schied im Sinn, der Ab - schied vom Schwarzwälder Tal.

1. A mill by the brook in a Black Forest vale,
Stands charmingly, clicking its wheels.
Where ere I rest or go,
Through mountains high and low,
There's always the mill in the vale on my mind,
The mill in the Black Forest vale.

2. And there in the mill in the Black Forest vale,
Is living a girl, oh so fair,
And where I rest or go,
Through mountains high and low,
There's always the girl from the mill on my mind,
The girl from the Black Forest vale.

3. In parting we stood there,
Hands clasping once more;
And wishing each other God's speed.
Now where I rest or go,
Through mountains high and low,
There's always the parting from her on my mind,
The parting from the Black Forest vale.

128

Im Wald und auf der Heide

The Forest and the Heather

1. Im Wald und auf der Heide, da such ich meine Freude, ich bin ein Jägersmann, ich bin ein Jägers-mann. Den Wald und Forst zu hegen, das Wildbret zu er-le-gen, mein' Lust hab ich dar-an, mein' Lust hab ich dar-an. Hal-li, hal-lo, hal-li, hal-lo, mein Lust hab ich dar-an.

2. Und streif ich durch die Wälder
und zieh ich durch die Felder
||: allein den ganzen Tag, :||
so schwinden mir die Stunden
gleich flüchtigen Sekunden,
||: tracht ich dem Wilde nach. :||
||: Halli, hallo, halli, hallo,
tracht ich dem Wilde nach. :||

3. Wenn sich die Sonne neiget,
der feuchte Nebel steiget,
||: mein Tagwerk ist getan. :||
Dann zieh ich von der Heide
zur häuslich stillen Freude,
||: ein froher Jägersmann. :||
||: Halli, hallo, halli, hallo,
ein froher Jägersmann. :||

1. The woods and fields I treasure
And find in them my pleasure,
||: A gamesman I'm by trade. :||
Of forest I take care
And hunt the deer and bear,
||: This is my joy and fate. :||
|| Halli, hallo, halli, hallo,
This is my joy and fate. :||

2. When strolling through the woodlands
And wandering through the mountains
||: Alone, no day's the same, :||
Then hours seem like seconds,
Time swiftly flies and beckons
||: To watch and stalk the game :||
Halli, hallo, halli, hallo,
To watch and stalk the game. :||

3. And when the sun is setting
And mists rise like fine netting
||: My day's work then is done. :||
Fulfilled has been my yearning
And homeward I am turning
||: A happy huntingman :||
||: Halli, hallo, halli, hallo,
A happy huntingman. :||

Jetzt Ist die Zeit und Stunde da

The Time and Hour is Now at Hand

Jetzt ist die Zeit und Stun- de da. Dass wir ziehn nach A-me-ri- ka. Viel tau-send See- len geht's dort gut Das trös- tet uns und gibt uns Mut.

Instructions

Verses 1, 2, 3, 5, 6 and 7 start at the beginning.

Verses 4 and 8 begin at ₵.

2. Die Wagen stehn schon vor der Tür.
Mit Weib und Kindern ziehen wir.
Die Pferde stehn schon angespannt,
Wir ziehen in ein fremdes Land.

3. Ihr alle die mit uns verwandt,
Reicht uns zum letzten mal die Hand.
Ihr Freunde weinet nicht zu sehr,
wir sehn uns nun, und nimmer mehr.

₵ 4. Seid alle männlich, und seid stark,
Macht uns den Abschied nicht zu hart
Wir ziehen ja nicht aus der Welt,
Auch da ist Gott, der uns erhält.

5. Wenn unser Schiff zur See einschwimmt,
Dann werden Lieder angestimmt.
Wir fürchten keinen Wasserfall,
Der Liebe Gott ist überall.

6. Und kommen wir gen Baltimor,
Dann heben wir das Land empor,
Und rufen laut "Victoria"!
Jetzt sind wir in America.

7. Willkommen fremdes Vaterland,
Wo sich mein Herz hat hin gewandt.
Du Land wo ich geboren bin,
Muss meiden und muss weit dahin.

₵ 8. Leb wohl du altes Vaterland,
Lebt alle wohl die uns gekannt,
Wir werden uns einst wiedersehn,
Dort wo die Friedens-Palmen wehn.

1. The time and hour is now at hand,
   We're moving to a foreign land.
   Where souls by thousands prosper well,
   Dauntless, with tears, we say farewell.

2. Our wagons loaded stand in a row,
   With wives and children we shall go.
   Our horses hitched to wagons stand,
   We're leaving for an unknown land.

3. To our beloved ones and our kin,
   We say farewell, and sigh within;
   Weep not so hard that we must part,
   It grieves our weary saddened heart.

4. Be manly and renew your strength,
   As time goes on, we'll meet at length.
   We still remain upon this sphere,
   Where God's protection will be near.

5. When we embark the ship at sea
   We'll join in songs of jubilee;
   We fear no water and no waves,
   For God is there and His love saves.

6. When we'll arrive on yonder shore,
   God's holy name we will adore;
   We'll shout, when we step on the strand,
   America, thou blessed land.

7. Welcome thou Fatherland afar,
   Where favored gates stand wide ajar.
   We now our land of birth disown,
   We've chosen a home in lands unknown.

8. Farewell, farewell, my Fatherland,
   Farewell, again, my kindred band;
   Some day we'll meet on heaven's shore,
   'Neath peaceful Palms forever more.

131

Kein schőner Land

No Fairer Land

1. Kein schő-ner Land in die-ser Zeit als hier das uns-re weit und breit, wo wir uns fin-den wohl un-ter Lin-den zur A-bend-zeit, wo wir uns fin-den wohl un-ter Lin-den zur A-bend-zeit.

2. Da haben wir so manche Stund
gesessen da in froher Rund
und taten singen,
die Lieder klingen
im Eichengrund.

3. Daß wir uns hier in diesem Tal
noch treffen sovielhundertmal:
Gott mag es schenken,
Gott mag es lenken,
er hat die Gnad.

4. Jetzt, Brüder, eine gute Nacht!
Der Herr im hohen Himmel wacht;
in seiner Güte
uns zu behüten,
ist er bedacht.

1. No fairer place, by far and near,
Is just like ours, we hold it dear,
||: Where by the linden tree,
We gather oft and free,
At evening time. :||

2. We come together happily,
Sit down beneath the lovely tree,
||: To start our singing,
The sounds are ringing
At evening time. :||

3. God grant that we, in time and space,
May long enjoy this peaceful place.
||: We trust His guiding,
And His providing,
It is His grace. :||

4. We say, "good night" and take our hands,
And pray to God to guard our lands.
||: His love is ever near,
To our friends so dear,
And each one here. :||

132

Morgenrot

Morning Light

1. Mor - gen - rot, Mor - gen - rot, leuchtest mir zum frühen Tod?
2. Kaum gedacht, kaum gedacht, war der Lust ein End' ge - macht.
3. Ach, wie bald, ach, wie bald schwindet Schön - heit und Ge - stalt!
4. Dar - um still, dar - um still füg' ich mich. wie Gott es will.

leuchtest mir
war der Lust
schwindet Schön -
füg' ich mich

Bald wird die Trom - pe - te bla - sen, dann muss ich mein Le - ben
Ge - stern noch auf stol - zen Ros - sen, heu - te durch die Brust ge -
Tust du stolz mit dei - nen Wan - gen, die mit Milch und Pur - pur
Nun, so will ich wa - cker strei - ten, und sollt' ich den Tod er -

las - sen, ich und man - - cher Ka - me - rad!
schos - sen, mor - gen in das küh - le Grab!
pran - gen? Ach, die Ro - - sen wel - ken all!
lei - den, stirbt ein bra - - ver Rei - ters - mann.

ich und man -
mor - gen in
Ach, die Ro -
stirbt ein bra -

1. ‖: Morning light, Morning light!
   Shall I meet with death ere night?:‖
   ‖: Soon we'll hear the bugle blowing,
   'T is to death we may be going,
   I and many a comrade brave!:‖

2. ‖: Scarce begun, scarce begun,
   Is a pleasure ere 't is done!:‖
   ‖: Yesterday on chargers flying,
   Shot to-day, and surely dying,
   And to-morrow in the grave!:‖

3. ‖: Yet ye maids, yet ye maids,
   Soon your grace and beauty fades.:‖
   ‖: Tho' your cheeks to-day are glowing
   Pink and white, like roses growing,
   Like the roses they will fade.:‖

4. ‖: Silently, silently,
   I submit, God's will may be. :‖
   ‖: Bravely will I fight as ever
   And if death there I should suffer,
   A brave cavalry man I'll be. :‖

Nun ade, du mein lieb' Heimatland

Farewell, Oh My Dear Fatherland

1. Nun a-de, du mein lieb' Hei-mat-land, lieb' Hei-mat-land, a-de! Es geht jetzt fort zum fer-nen Strand, lieb' Hei-mat-land, a-de! Und so sing' ich denn mit fro-hem Mut, wie man sin-get, wenn man wan-dern tut, lieb' Hei-mat-land, a-de.

2. Wie du lachst mit dei-nes Him-mels Blau, lieb' Hei-mat-land, a-de! Wie du grü-ßest mich mit Feld und Au', lieb' Hei-mat-land, a-de! Gott weiß, zu dir steht stets mein Sinn; doch jetzt ziehts mich zur Fer-ne hin, lieb' Hei-mat-land, a-de.

3. Be-glei-test mich, du lie-ber Fluß, lieb' Hei-mat-land, a-de! Bist trau-rig, daß ich wan-dern muß, lieb' Hei-mat-land, a-de! Vom moos'-gen Stein am wald'-gen Tal, da grüß' ich dich zum letz-ten-mal, lieb' Hei-mat-land, a-de.

1. Farewell, oh my dear Fatherland, dear Fatherland, farewell.
I want to try fresh wind and sand, dear Fatherland, farewell.
So I wander, singing heartily,
As one sings when one feels strong and free,
Dear Fatherland, farewell.

2. How your sky looks down in heavenly blue, dear Fatherland, farewell.
And your trees and meadows fresh with dew, dear Fatherland, farewell.
God knows to you I'll faithful be,
But now the far lands beckon me,
Dear Fatherland, farewell.

3. Follow me awhile, oh river dear, dear Fatherland, farewell.
You are sad now that I part from here, dear Fatherland, farewell.
From this mossy rock without delay,
Let me greet you one last time today,
Dear Fatherland, farewell.

Seht, wie die Sonne dort sinket

See How the Sun Now is Sinking

1. Seht, wie die Son-ne dort sin-ket hin-ter dem nächt-li-chen Wald!
2. Hört ihr das Blö-ken der Läm-mer? Küh-len-de Lüf-te schon wehn!
3. Dörf-chen, o sei uns will-kom-men! Heut ist die Ar-beit voll-bracht,

Glöck-lein schon Ru-he uns win-ket; hört nur, wie lieb-lich es schallt.)
Se-het, es fängt an zu däm-mern, las-set zur Hüt-te uns gehn!
bald wird, von Ster-nen um-schwommen, na-hen die ru-hi-ge Nacht.

Trau-li-ches Glöcklein, du läutest so schön! Trauli-ches Glöcklein, du läutest so schön!

Läu-te, mein Glöcklein, nur zu, läu-te zur sü-ßen Ruh!

1. See how the sun now is sinking
Deeper behind distant hills.
Evening bell softly is ringing
Sweetly the air 'round us fills.

2. Little lambs wearily bleating,
Breezes are cooling the day.
Dusk falling, sunlight is fleeting,
Home let us turn our way.

3. Hamlet you make us feel cozy
Now that today's work is done.
Stars, like a heavenly posy,
Show us that night has begun.

Chorus
Evening bell's sound kissing gently the world.
Pealing and tolling it's best,
Ringing for peaceful rest.

Repeat

Schön ist die Jugend

Youth, O How Beautiful

1. Schön ist die Ju - gend bei fro - hen Zei - ten, schön ist die Ju - gend, sie kommt nicht
2. Es blüht der Wein - stock und der trägt Re - ben und aus den Re - ben, fliesst ed - ler
3. Es blüht ein Rosenstock und der trägt Ro - sen und aus den Ro - sen weht sü - sser

mehr! Es flieh'n die Ta - ge, es flieh'n die Jah - re, die Zei - ten
Wein! Und aus dem Wei - ne strömt Ju - gend - won - ne, doch bald ver -
Duft! Die Ro - sen blü - hen, die Ro - sen wel - ken, und wel - ke

wer - den dem Al - ter schwer.)
rausch sie, 's muss ja so sein.} Drum sag' ich's noch ein - mal: Schön sind die
Ro - sen sind oh - ne Duft.

Ju - gendjahr', schön ist die Ju - gend, sie kommt nicht mehr, sie kommt nicht

mehr, nicht mehr; ja, sie kommt nimmermehr, schön ist die Ju - gend, sie kommt nicht mehr.

1. Youth O how beautiful in times of pleasure
   Youth O how beautiful ne'er to return;
   The days are fleeing; the years are passing.
   The time has now arrived for you to yearn.

Chorus

   Therefore I say once more, Youth O how beautiful
   Youth O how glorious, too soon is gone,
   Too soon is gone, t'is gone,
   Never to come again,
   Youth O how beautiful but soon is gone.

2. There blooms a grapevine
   That carries branches
   And from the branches flows noble wine,
   And from the noble wine streams youthful rapture
   Yet soon to vanish is its design.

3. There blooms a rose bush and it
   bears roses and from the roses
   wafts fragrant scent.
   Roses are blooming and roses wither
   And wilted roses, they have no scent.

Ve Cherni Zvon

137

Tief im Böhmerwald

Deep in the Bohemian Woods

1. Tief in dem Böh - mer-wald, da liegt mein Hei - mat-ort, es ist gar
2. O hol - de Kin - des-zeit, noch ein - mal kehr zu - rück, wo spie - lend
3. Nur ein - mal noch, o Herr, laß mich die Hei - mat sehn, den schö - nen

lang' schon her, daß ich von dort bin fort. Doch die Er - in - ne-rung, die bleibt mir
ich ge - noß das al - ler - höch - ste Glück, wo ich am Va - ter-haus auf grü - ner
Böh - merwald, die Tä - ler und die Höhn, dann kehr' ich gern zu-rück und ru - fe

stets ge - wiß, daß ich den Böh - merwald gar nie ver - giß.
Wie - se stand und weit-hin schau - te auf mein Va - ter - land.
freu - dig aus: Be - hüt dich, Böh - merwald, ich bleib' zu Haus.

Es war im

Böh - merwald, wo mei - ne Wie - ge stand, im schö - nen, grü - nen Böh - merwald, es war im

Böh - merwald, wo mei - ne Wie - ge stand, im schö - nen, grü - nen Wald.

1. My home stands deep in the Bohemian Forest hills
And the remembrance fond my longing heart now fills.
From there I left a long, long time ago, and yet —
My dear Bohemian Woods I'll n'er forget.

Chorus

In the Bohemian Woods 'tis where my cradle stood,
The beautiful Bohemian Woods
In the Bohemian Woods 'tis where my cradle stood,
Those green and lovely woods.

2. O precious childhood years, once more come back to bless,
Where playing I enjoyed the greatest happiness.
Where, by my father's house, in pastures green I stood
And saw my fatherland, a place so good.

3. Let me once more, O Lord, my beloved homeland see
Bohemian Woods and hills and valleys dear to me.
With joy will I return and shout the glad refrain
Bless you, Bohemian Woods, here I'll remain.

Ich hatt' einen Kameraden

I Had a Comrade

2. Eine Kugel kam geflogen,
   gilt sie mir oder gilt sie dir?
   Ihn hat es weggerissen,
   er liegt zu meinen Füssen,
   als wär's ein Stück von mir.
   als war's ein Stück von mir.

3. Will mir die Hand noch reichen
   derweil ich eben lad.
   "Kann dir die Hand nicht geben,
   bleib du im ewgen Leben
   mein guter Kamerad!
   mein guter Kamerad!"

1. ‖: I had a trusty comrade,
      None else so true and tried;:‖
   ‖: The drums began to rattle,
      We marched away to battle
      In step and side by side,
      In step and side by side.:‖

2. A bullet came a-whizzing,
   Was't billed for him or me?
   Away from me it snatched him
   And at my feet it stretched him,
   As though a part of me!

3. His hand he tries to reach me,
   As I my charge renew;
   My hand was never given,
   But he will be in heaven
   My comrade tried and true!

Tränen hab' ich viele, viele vergossen

I've Wept Many, Many Tears

Trä - nen hab ich vie - le, vie - le ver-gos-sen, weil ich
Doch mein lie - ber Va - ter hatt es be-schlos-sen: aus der

schei-den muss von hier; Hei - mat heu - te wan - dern wir. Heut auf
Hei - mat wan-dern wir, Drum ad - je, so le - bet wohl! Drum ad-

e - wig von dir, Drum ad - je so le - bet wohl!
je, ad - je, ad - je, Drum ad - je so le - bet wohl!

2. Lebet wohl, ihr meine Rosen im Garten,
Und ihr, meine Blümelein!
Darf euch nicht weiter pflegen und warten,
Denn es muss geschieden sein!
Liebe Blümlein, weint mit mir,
Heute scheide ich von hier.

1. I've wept many, many tears
Since I must part from here;
But my father has decided
That we leave our homeland.
Homeland, today we shall leave you
Today, we leave forever.

Chorus:
So goodbye and farewell!
So adieu, adieu, adieu,
So adieu, adieu, adieu,
So goodbye and farewell!

2. Farewell, you roses in the garden
And you, my little flowers!
I can tend and keep you no longer
For we now have to part!
Dear flowers, weep with me.
Today I'm leaving from here.

140

Trara, die Post ist da

Hurrah, the Mail is Here

Tra - ra, die Post ist da! Tra - ra, die Post ist da! Von weitem hör' ich schon den Ton, Sein
Hur - rah, the mail is here! Hur - rah, the mail is here! From far a - way the sound I hear, The

Liedchen blast der Pos - til - lon, Er bläst mit starker Kehle, Er bläst aus froher Seele; die
Coachman's song so loud and clear. He blows the hearty shrill, He blows with happy soul. The

Das Posthorn tönt

Post ist da, tra - ra, tra - ra, die Post ist da trara!
mail is here, Hur - rah, hur-rah, The mail is here, Hurrah!

141

Treue Liebe

True Love

1. Ach, wie ist's mög-lich dann, daß ich dich las-sen kann; hab dich von Her-zen lieb, das glau-be mir! Du hast die See-le mein so ganz ge-nom-men ein, daß ich kein and-re lieb, als dich al-lein!

2. Blau blüht ein Blü-me-lein, das heißt Ver-giß-nicht-mein: dies Blüm-lein leg ans Herz und den-ke mein! Stirbt Blum' und Hoff-nung gleich, wir sind an Lie-be reich, denn sie stirbt nie bei mir, das glau-be mir!

3. Wär' ich ein Vö-ge-lein, bald wollt' ich bei dir sein, scheut' Falk' und Ha-bicht nicht, flög' schnell zu dir! Schöß' mich ein Jä-ger tot, fiel ich in dei-nen Schoß: sähst du mich trau-rig an, gern stürb ich dann.

1. How can I leave thee so?
   How can I bear to go?
   Thou know'st how well I love:
      Trust me, mine own!
   Thou, dear, this heart of mine,
   Hast made so wholly thine,
   None other could I love,
      But thee alone.

2. Blue is the flower I've brought,
   'T is called Forget-me-not;
   Lay this against thine heart,
      And think of me.
   Tho' flower and hope should die
   Rich, dear, art thou and I
   In love, that on my part
      Deathless shall be!

3. If I a bird could be,
   Soon should I come to thee,
   Falcon nor hawk I'd fear,
      To thee I'd fly.
   Fell I, by fowler pressed,
   Dying upon thy breast,
   Didst thou but shed a tear,
      Gladly I'd die.

Üb' immer Treu und Redlichkeit

May Honesty and Truth Abide

1. Üb im - mer Treu und Red - lich-keit bis an dein küh - les Grab, und
2. Dann wirst du wie auf grü - nen Au'n durchs Pil - ger - le - ben gehn; dann
3. Dann wird die Si - chel und der Pflug in dei - ner Hand so leicht; dann
4. Dem Bö - se-wicht wird al - les schwer; er tu - e was er tu'; das

1. wei - che kei - nen Fin - ger breit von Got - tes We - gen ab.
2. kannst du oh - ne Furcht und Grau'n dem Tod ins Au - ge sehn.
3. sin - gest du beim Was - ser-krug, als wär dir Wein ge - reicht.
4. La - ster treibt ihn hin und her und läßt ihm kei - ne Ruh.

5. Der schöne Frühling lacht ihm nicht, ihm lacht kein Ährenfeld;
Er ist auf Lug and Trug erpicht und wünscht sich nichts als Geld.

6. Der Wind im Hain, das Laub am Baum saust ihm Entsetzen zu;
Er findet nach des Lebens Traum im Grabe keine Ruh.

7. Drum übe Treu und Redlichkeit bis an dein kühles Grab,
Und weiche keinen Finger breit von Gottes Wegen ab.

8. Dann suchen Enkel deine Gruft und weinen Tränen drauf,
Und Sommerblumen voller Duft blühn aus den Tränen auf.

1. May honesty and truth abide
With you until you die,
Not even stray a finger wide
From God's appointed way.

Synopsis of Verses 2 through 8

The honest person is a free man, can enjoy work and play, needs to fear nothing, not even death. But the wicked are not happy. They are slaves of their bad habits. They feel haunted and cannot find peace, even in the grave.

Therefore, always practice truth and honesty. Never waiver. Then your grandchildren will come to your grave and shed tears. And out of those tears will grow fragrant summer flowers.

143

Und in dem Schneegebirge

High in the Snow-Capped Mountains

1. Und in dem Schnee-ge-bir-ge, da fließt ein Brünn-lein kalt; und wer das Brünn-lein trin-ket, und wer das Brünn-lein trin-ket, wird jung und nim-mer alt.

2. Ich hab dar-aus ge-trun-ken gar man-chen fri-schen Trunk; ich bin nicht alt ge-wor-den, ich bin nicht alt ge-wor-den, ich bin noch all-zeit jung.

3. A-de, mein Schatz, ich schei-de, a-de, mein Schät-ze-lein! „Wann kommst du a-ber wie-der, wann kommst du a-ber wie-der, Herz-al-ler-lieb-ster mein?"

4. Wenn's schneiet rote Rosen
Und regnet kühlen Wein.
||: Ade, mein Schatz, ich scheide, :||
Ade, mein Schätzelein.

5. "Es schneit ja keine Rosen
Und regnet keinen Wein:
||: So kommst du auch nicht wieder, :||
Herzallerliebster mein!"

1. High in the snow-capped mountains
There flows a brook so cold
||:And he who goes and drinks it:||
Grows young and never old.

2. I went to drink it freely,
It felt so cool on my tongue
||:I never did grow older:||
I am forever young.

3. Farewell, my love, I leave you,
Farewell my sweetheart dear.
||:"When will you come to see me:||
Oh my beloved, here?"

4. When it will snow red roses
And then rain cool red wine.
||:Farewell, my love, I leave you:||
Farewell, Oh sweetheart mine.

5. It never snows red roses
And never rains cool wine,
||:So you'll be not returning:||
To me, beloved mine.

Unterländers Heimweh

Lowlander's Longing

1. ||:Down in the Lowland all's open and free!:||
   ||:Up in the Highland, snow!
      Grapes in the Lowland grow:
   Down in the Lowland is where I would be:||

2. ||:Down by the Neckar they do things with style;:||
   ||:Sometimes — for I'll be fair —
      They do have fun, up there:
   Down here I have a good time all the while:||

3. ||:Cold are the Uplands, the Lowland is warm:||
   ||:Up there they have the gold;
      My! but their hearts are cold:
   Look at you coolly, and never wax warm.:||

4. ||:But to be poor, down here, does one no harm.:||
   ||:Here men are tried and true,
      Here girls will stick to you:
   That's why the Lowlander's heart is so warm.:||

145

Vespergesang

Vesper Song

1. Horch die Wel-len tra-gen be-bend sanft und rein den Ves-per-chor;
nä-her jetzt und nä-her schwebend schwillt er mäch-tig zu dem Ohr:

2. Wie die Mondlicht-wel-le keh-ret von dem Stran-de, stirbt's ent-lang;
wie die Flut sich wild em-pö-ret, braust der wo-gen-de Ge-sang:

Ju-bi-la-te, ju-bi-la-te, ju-bi-la-te, A-men.

3. Fer-ner nun und fer-ner be-bend, horch jetzt, wie die Wo-ge keh-ret
sanft entschwindet der Ge-sang; von dem Stran-de, stirbt's ent-lang!

Ju-bi-la-te, ju-bi-la-te, ju-bi-la-te, A-men.

1. Listen how the waves are bearing gently our vesper song;
   Floating close, softly swelling, soaring now, mighty and strong;
   Jubilate, jubilate, jubilate, Amen.

2. Soft as moonlight on a ripple fading into nothingness;
   Then returning like a flood wave rushing full of joyfulness:
   Jubilate, jubilate, jubilate, Amen.

3. Ebb and flow like rolling waters ever more the melody;
   Wavelike falling and then rising rings our song in harmony:
   Jubilate, jubilate, jubilate, Amen.

Weisse Akazien

White Acacias

Weis - se A - ka - zi - en duf - ten die gan - ze Nacht
Weis - se A - ka - zi - en hat - ten mein Herz be - tört
Weis - se A - ka - zi - en blü - hen in je - dem Jahr

brin - gen die Ju - gend mir _____ zu - rück.
als ich zum er - sten - mal _____ sie sah.
im - mer noch schlägt die Nach - ti - gall.

In sanf - tem Blü - ten - wind bin ich vom Schlaf er - wacht
Der dich - te Blü - ten - busch hat un - sern Schwur ge - hört
Die Zeit ist längst vor - bei, in der ich glück - lich war.

träu - me von al - ter Zeit, von fer - nem Glück. _____
und ei - ne Nach - ti - gall sang süss und nah.
Wo blieb der Lie - be Glück, der Lie - be Qual? _____

1. Sweetest acacias scenting throughout the night,
   Recall to me my joyful youth.
   Their fragrant tenderness around my deepest sleep.
   Bring dreams of distant youth and happiness.

2. Sweetest acacias my heart you swept away
   When first your sweetness I beheld.
   Your compact blossom form has yielded to my vow.
   And nightingales were heard to sing nearby.

3. Sweetest acacias blossom in every year.
   Still ever sings the Nightingale.
   The time has swiftly passed when I so happy lived.
   Oh where is happy love! Oh painful love!

"Akazien" in German in actuality
   translates to "Locust" (trees) in English.

Wenn die Schwalben heimwärts ziehn

When the Swallows Homeward Fly

1. Wenn die Schwal - ben heimwärts ziehn und die Ro - sen nicht mehr blühn, wenn der
2. Wenn die Schwä - ne süd - lich ziehn, dorthin wo Zi - tro - nen blühn, wenn das
3. Ar - mes Herz, was kla-gest du? o, auch du gehst einst zur Ruh! Was auf

Nach - ti - gall Ge - sang mit der Nach-ti-gall ver-klang, fragt das
A - bendrot ver - sinkt, durch die grü-nen Wäl - der blinkt, fragt das
Er - den, muß ver - gehn: gibt es wohl ein Wie - der-sehn? Fragt das

Herz in bangem Schmerz, fragt das Herz in bangem Schmerz: ob ich
Herz in bangem Schmerz, fragt das Herz in bangem Schmerz: ob ich
Herz in bangem Schmerz, fragt das Herz in bangem Schmerz: Glaub', daß

dich auch wie - der - seh? Schei-den, ach, Schei - den,
dich auch wie - der - seh? Schei-den, ach, Schei - den,
ich dich wie - der - seh, tut auch heut das

Scheiden tut weh! Schei - den,ach,Schei - den, Scheiden tut weh!
Scheiden tut weh! Schei - den,ach,Schei - den, Scheiden tut weh!
Scheiden so weh, tut auch heut das Scheiden so weh!

1. When the swallows homeward fly,
   When the roses scatter'd lie,
   When from neither hill or dale,
   Chants the silv'ry nightingale
   In these words my bleeding heart,
   Would to thee it's grief impart.
   When I thus thy image lose.
   Can I, ah! can I e'er know repose,
   Can I, ah! Can I e'er know repose.

2. When the white swan southward roves,
   Seeks at noon the orange groves,
   When the red tints of the west,
   Drove the sun, is gone to rest;
   In these words my bleeding heart,
   Would to thee it's grief impart.
   When I thus thy image lose.
   Can I ah! can I e'er know repose,
   Can I, ah! Can I e'er know repose.

Das schőne Frűhjahr

The Lovely Springtime

1. Jetzt fängt das schö - ne Frűh - jahr an, und al - les fängt zu blü - hen an auf grü - ner Heid und ű - ber- - all.

2. Es blűhen Blűmlein auf dem Feld,
   Sie blűhen weiss, blau, rot und gelb,
   Es gibt nichts Schőners auf der Welt.

3. Jetzt geh ich ű ber Berg und Tal,
   Da singt so schőn Frau Nachtigall
   Auf grűner Heid und űberall.

4. Und wenn ich durch die Auen geh,
   Da singt das Lerchlein in der Hőh,
   Weil ich zu meinem Schätzle geh.

1. The lovely springtime now is here
   and all is blooming far and near
   in hill and dale and everywhere.

2. The flowers in the fields around
   in brilliant colors all abound
   no greater loveliness the world has seen.

3. I wander now through hill and dale
   Melodious sings Miss Nightingale
   in yonder glen and everywhere.

149

Mein Heimatland

Nur einmal noch möcht' ich dich wiedersehen,
O du mein liebes, trautes Heimatland,
Nur einmal noch an deiner Schwelle stehen,
Du heil'ger Ort, wo meine Wiege stand;
Nur einmal noch auf deinen trauten Fluren
Verfolgen meiner frohen Kindheit Spuren,
Dich wiederseh'n, wie ich dich einst gekannt,
    Mein Heimatland!

Einst träumte ich, ich hätte dich gefunden;
Ich kehrte heim ins Vaterhaus zurück!
Wie schnell war all das bittre Weh geschwunden.
O, wer beschreibt mein unaussprechlich Glück!
Ich musste lachen, weinen, danken, singen,
Das Herz wollt' mir vor Freude springen.
Doch ach, wie schwand das Glück, ich wusst' es kaum:
    's war nur ein Traum.

Doch bin ich auch aus deinem Schoss gerissen,
Verschmachtet auch im fremden Land mein Herz,
Ja, du hast selbst wohl meiner längst vergessen
Und kein Gefühl für meinen bittren Schmerz,
So sing ich dir mein Lied doch alle Tage,
So schlägt mein Herz dir doch mit jedem Schlage,
So wird mein letzter Gruss doch dir gesandt,
    Mein Heimatland.

Sei still, mein Herz, es sind nicht Deutschlands Fluren,
Auf denen Friede winkt und Glück dir blüht.
Es sind des grossen Heilands Retterspuren,
Und seine Lieb', die an sein Herz dich zieht.
Da wird gar bald verstummen alles Klagen,
Wenn du, auf deines Hirten Arm getragen,
Erblicken wirst den sel'gen Himmelsstrand,
    Mein Vaterland.

        Pastor C. G. Meyer

Glück

Ein Hüttlein, von alten Bäumen bewacht,
Ein Kind, das in goldener Gesundheit lacht,
Ein braves Weib und ein Stücklein Feld —
Das ist das herrlichste Glück auf der Welt!

Happiness

A cottage guarded by lovely old trees,
A child who in radiant health one sees,
A faithful wife and a piece of ground —
Therein is the greatest happiness found!

Froh zu sein bedarf es wenig, und wer froh ist, ist ein König.

(Canon)

Wolgalied

1. Auf der Wolga breiten Fluten
   durch das enge Tuseltor
   bricht auf buntbemaltem Boote
   Steuke Rassius Schar hervor.

2. Auf dem ersten mit der Fürstin
   seiner schönen Perserin
   zieht nach festlich heitrem Mahle
   frohgessinnt er selbst dahin.

3. Und es geht ein leises Grollen
   durch der Donkossaken Reih'n,
   soll um eines Weibes willen
   Unsre Not vergessen sein?

4. Und sie spotten selbst zum Weibe
   hatten Helden sie gemacht,
   Steuka hört es, und der alte Recke
   ist in ihm erwacht.

5. Um den schlanken Leib der Schönen
   legt er fester nun den Arm,
   fragend blickt sie auf zum Liebsten
   "Wirkt mir Freude oder Harm?"

6. Steuka schweigt, es blinkt sein Auge,
   dir mein Wolga Mütterlein.
   Wolga, schönster aller Ströme,
   niemals war solch Kleinod dein.

7. Finster zuckt's um seine Brauen
   wilde Wetter ziehn heran
   ja, jetzt bist du Steuka wieder
   der Kossaken Atamann.

8. "Wohl ich will zum Opfer bringen
   was mir lieb auf dieser Welt,"
   schreit er laut mit Donnerstimme,
   dass es rauh zum Ufer gellt.

9. "Dass sich unter freien Männern
   nicht mehr so ein Zwist entspinn',
   nimm du schöne Wolga, Wolga,
   Mutter Wolga, nimm sie hin."

10. Und er hebt mit kühnem Schwunge
    seine Fürstin über Bord,
    schleudert weit sie in die Fluten
    und die Wolga trägt sie fort.

11. "Nun was lasst den Kopf ihr hängen?
    Brüder stimmt ein Lied geschwind,
    und ein Räub'r lied Kameraden,
    das zur Ehr ihr hell erklingt."

12. Auf der Wolga breiten Fluten
    durch das enge Tuseltor
    bricht auf buntbemaltem Boote
    Steuke Rassius Schar hervor.

Wolgalied

Aus der schönen Stadt Saratov
drang in unser Steppenreich
laute Botschaft, alle Männer
sollten sich versammeln gleich.

Sollten mit den Russenwaffen
ausziehn in den Kaiser Streit,
auf die deutschen Brüder schiessen
und sie morden weit und breit.

Vierzigtausend Kolonisten
zogen in den schweren Krieg,
sollten Russland Treue halten,
beten doch für Deutschland's Sieg.

Flehten: Wolga bringe Frieden
wieder in das Steppenreich,
segne Deutschland, segne Russland,
segne unser Wolgareich.

Wolga, liebe Wolga
Unser heisses Herzeleid
Halte fern vom Wolga-Deutschland
Neuen Krieg in Ewigkeit.

151

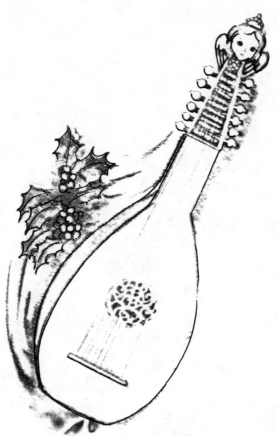

Fest-Lieder

Amerika, o schön bist du

America the Beautiful

1. O, schön bist du! Ein wo-gend Meer Das Korn im Gol - des - glanz;

2. O, schön bist du! Aus dumpfer Haft Hat dir durchs Ur - wald - grau'n

3. O, schön bist du! Manch ed - ler Sohn Der neu-durch-glüh-ten Zeit

Weit, weit die Tä - ler, früch-te-schwer, In stol - zer Ber - ge Kranz

Der Pil - ger-va - ter Op - fer-kraft Den Pfad zum Licht ge - hau'n

Träumt dich ein Tal des Friedens schon, Stumm all dein seufzend Leid

A - mer - i - ka! A - mer - i - ka! Wann weht von Strand zu Strand

A - mer - i - ka! A - mer - i - ka! Gott mach' dein Herz ge - treu

A - mer - i - ka! A - mer - i - ka! Wann flammt von Strand zu Strand

Der Bru - der - geist, durch den du weihst Zur Got - tes - flur dein Land?

Dem heil' - gen Licht der in - nern Pflicht Und im Ge - hor - sam frei!

Der Bru - der - geist, durch den du weihst Zum Got-tes - reich dein Land?

1. Oh, beautiful for spacious skies,
   For amber waves of grain,
   For purple mountains majesties
   Above the fruited plain!
   America! America!
   God shed His grace on thee,
   And crown thy good with brotherhood
   From sea to shining sea!

2. Oh, beautiful for pilgrim feet,
   Whose stern, impassioned stress
   A thoroughfare for freedom beat
   Across the wilderness!
   America! America!
   God mend thine ev'ry flaw,
   Confirm thy soul in self-control,
   Thy liberty in law!

3. Oh, beautiful for patriot dream
   That sees beyond the years
   Thine alabaster cities gleam,
   Undimmed by human tears!
   America! America!
   God shed His grace on thee,
   And crown thy good with brotherhood
   From sea to shining sea!

Dir sing ich, Vaterland

America

1. Dir sing' ich, Va-ter-land, Der Frei-heit Hei-mat-land, A-me-ri-ka! Zu der Ver-folg-ten Port, Der Un-ter-drück-ten Hort, Zur Wohn-statt für sein Wort Gott dich er-sah.

2. Land frei-er Män-ner du, Froh jauchzt mein Herz dir zu, Wie bist du hehr! Hoch dei-ne Ber-ge steh'n, Stolz dei-ne Strö-me geh'n, Frei dei-ne Ban-ner weh'n Von Meer zu Meer.

3. Ur-quell der Frei-heit, Gott, Je-ho-vah Ze-ba-oth, Halt' du sie rein! Lass nicht der Sün-de Macht Hül-len ihr Licht in Nacht, Halt' sel-ber für uns Wacht, Kö-nig al-lein!

1. My country, 'tis of thee,
Sweet land of liberty,
Of thee I sing;
Land where my fathers died,
Land of the pilgrims' pride,
From every mountain side
Let freedom ring!

2. My native country, thee,
Land of the noble free,
Thy name I love;
I love thy rocks and rills,
Thy woods and templed hills;
My heart with rapture thrills
Like that above.

3. Our fathers' God to Thee,
Author of liberty,
To Thee we sing;
Long may our land be bright
With freedom's holy light;
Protect us by Thy might,
Great God, our King.

O Canada

O Kanada, mein Heim und Vaterland

Wie glücklich der, dem hier die Wiege stand

Das Herz erglüht, wenn wir dich seh'n

Du Nordland, stark und frei

Wir halten Wacht, O Kanada

Wir halten Wacht dir treu

Chorus:

O Kanada, O Kanada, O Kanada,

Wir halten Wacht dir treu

O Kanada, wir halten Wacht dir treu.

Wo Gott allein regiert

Battle Hymn of the Republic

1. O seht das Licht der Wahr-heit Auf den Ber-ges - hö - hen glühn; Seht es
2. Vom heitren Le - bens-mor-gen Bis zum A-bend-son-nen-strahl, Wol-len
3. Legt an des Gei-stes Waf-fen De-nen Erz und Stahl nicht gleicht, Nehmt das

strah-lend durch die Län - de Hin zum fern-sten Mee-re ziehn! Bis
wir uns treu - lich mü-hen In dem Werk das Gott be - fahl; Bis
schar - fe Schwert des Wor-tes, Das des Sün-ders Herz er - reicht; Bis

vor dem gold-nen Glan-ze Nacht und Finsternis entfliehn Und Gott allein regiert.
wir als Sie-ger zie-hen In des Himmels Freudensaal, Wo Gott allein regiert.
wir den Sieg er-run-gen Und die Macht der Sün de weicht Und Gott allein regiert.

Chorus

Glo-rie, Glorie, Hal-le-lu - jah! Glo - rie, Glo-rie, Hal-le - lu - jah!

Glo-rie, Glo-rie, Hal-le-lu - jah! Wenn Gott al - lein re - giert!

1. Mine eyes have seen the glory of the coming of the Lord,
He is trampling out the vintage where the grapes of wrath are stored;
He hath loosed the fateful lightning of His terrible swift sword,
His truth is marching on.

2. I have seen Him in the watchfires of a hundred circling camps.
They have builded Him an altar in the evening dews and damps;
I can read His righteous sentence by the dim and flaring lamps,
His day is marching on.

3. He has sounded forth the trumpet that shall never call retreat,
He is sifting out the hearts of men before His judgment seat;
O be swift, my soul, to answer Him, be jubilant, my feet!
Our God is marching on.

4. In the beauty of the lilies Christ was born across the sea.
With a glory in His bosom that transfigures you and me;
As He died to make men holy let us live to make men free!
While God is marching on.

Chorus

Glory! glory! Hallelujah! Glory! glory! Hallelujah!
Glory! glory! Hallelujah! His truth is marching on!

Christus ist erstanden heut

Christ the Lord is Risen Today

1. Chri-stus ist er-stan-den heut, Froh das Sie-ges-lied er-neut;

2. Lie-be hat ihr Werk voll-bracht, Ü-ber-wand des Fein-des Macht;

3. Nutz-los Wäch-ter, Sie-gel, Stein, Denn ihn hüllt kein Grab-tuch ein;

4. Chri-stus lebt und wird nicht ruhn — Tod, wo ist dein Sta-chel nun?

Him-mel, stim-me an den Preis, Jub-le mit, o Er-den-kreis!

Uns-re Son-ne strah-let auf, E-wig währt ihr hel-ler Lauf.

Sieg-reich er die Gruft ver-liess, Öff-net uns das Pa-ra-dies.

Uns zum Heil er hin sich gab — Wo ist nun dein Sieg, o Grab?

1. Christ, the Lord, is ris'n today,
Sons of men and angels say:
Raise your joys and triumphs high,
Sing, ye heav'ns, and earth, reply.

2. Love's redeeming work is done;
Fought the fight; the battle won:
Lo! our sun's eclipse is o'er;
Lo! he sets in blood no more.

3. Vain the stone, the watch, the seal —
Christ hath burst the gates of hell:
Death in vain forbids Him rise —
Christ hath opened Paradise.

4. Lives again our glorious King:
Where, O death, is now thy sting?
Once He died our souls to save:
Where's thy vict'ry, boasting grave?

Ich muss dich wiedersehn

I Must See You Again

1. Ver-ges-sen kann ich's nimmermehr, wie viel der Tränen sind, Die
2. Wo fand ich je so lin-de Hand, so liebreichernstes Wort, Wenn
3. Und als dein welt-be-tör-tes Kind den heim'schen Herd verliess Ein

einst mein gu-tes Müt-ter-lein ver-gos-sen um ihr Kind. Sie
Sün - den - lust und Sün-den-trotz mich riss zum Bö - sen fort? Wie
Sternlein blieb, das ihm den Weg zur ew'gen Hei-mat wies. Der

eil-te längst aus dieser Welt zu sel'gen Himmelshöhn. O Mütterlein, ich
konntest du dem bö'sen Kind so treu zur Seite stehn? O Mütterlein, ich
Stern dein Beten, liess mich nicht in Sündennot vergehn. O Mütterlein, ich

Chor.

muss dich wiedersehn [Dein Gebet war so heiss, war so innig; ich weiss: Es
                        Dein Gebet, Mutterherz, zog dein Kind himmelwärts. O

ward erhört, ich werd' dich wiedersehn.
Mütterlein, ich   muss dich wieder-sehn!

1. In all my life I'll ne'r forget
   The many tears I'd see
   That often times my mother dear
   Was shedding here for me.
   And then she left this earthly place
   To go to heaven's peace.
   Oh, Mother dear, I must see you again.

Chorus

But your prayer, I am sure, was so fervent and pure,
It was answered and I'll see you again.
Yes, your prayer, mother heart, leads your child heavenward.
Oh, Mother dear, I must see you again.

2. Where did I find a loving heart,
   Yet admonitions strong,
   When love of sin and stubbornness
   Would tempt me to do wrong?
   How could you be so patient and so ready to forgive?
   Oh, Mother dear, I must see you again.

3. And when your child, so world-enticed,
   Left home and hearth behind,
   A little star glowed deep inside
   To guide and change his mind.
   This star, your prayer, would not let me go too far astray
   Oh, Mother dear, I must see you again.

Danke Gott

Wenn du noch eine Mutter hast,	If your Mother you still have
So danke Gott und sei zufrieden,	Then thank your God and be well pleased.
Nicht Allen aus dem Erdenrund,	Not everyone around the world
Ist dieses hohe Glück beschieden.	Has been so wonderfully blessed.
Sie hat vom ersten Tage an	For from the outset of your days,
Für dich gelebt mit bangen Sorgen,	She watched o'er you with anxious eyes.
Sie brachte Abends dich zur Ruh'	At night she tucked you into bed
Und weckte küssend dich am Morgen.	And with a kiss at morning waked.
Und warst du krank, sie pflegte dein,	When you were ill, she cared for you
Den sie im tiefen Schmerz geboren;	Whom she in pain had given birth.
Und gaben Alle dich schon auf,	Though others faith in you may fail,
Die Mutter gab dich nicht verloren.	Your Mother still will know your worth.
Sie lehrte dir den frommen Spruch,	At first, she taught you how to speak
Sie lehrte dir zuerst das Reden;	Then, Bible verses to repeat.
Sie faltete die Hände dein	She trained you how your hands to fold
Und lehrte dich zum Vater beten.	And lift your prayers to Father, God.
Wenn du noch eine Mutter hast,	If your Mother you still have
So sollst du sie mit Liebe pflegen,	Confirm you love with constant care
Dass sie dereinst ihr müdes Haupt	That she one day her weary head
In Frieden kann zur Ruhe legen.	May lay to rest in calm repose.
Sie lenkte deinen Kindersinn,	She clearly trained your childhood ways
Sie wachte über deine Jugend;	And helped you through your youthful days.
Der Mutter danke es allein,	Most heartfelt thanks your Mother earned
wenn du noch gehst den Pfad der Tugend.	If you now walk the paths she formed.

Der Mutter Träne

Mother's Tear

1. Ich stand bei mei - ner Mut - ter, Die mich so herz-lich liebt,
   Sie war ganz still und trau - rig, Ich hat - te sie be - trübt.
2. Da fiel ein hei - sser Tro - pfen Her - ab auf mei - ne Hand;
   Er kam aus ih - rem Au - ge, Ich hab ihn wohl er-kannt.
3. Ich ha - be sie ver - stan - den, Wa - rum sie hat ge-weint,
   Und hab es tief em - pfun - den, Wie gut sie's mit mir meint.

Ich hat - te mei - ne Hän - de Auf ih - ren Schoss ge - legt,
Schnell stand sie auf, die Mut - ter, Und sprach da - bei kein Wort,
Nie will ich mehr be - trü - ben Das lie - be Mut - ter - herz.

War auch ganz still und trau - rig, Im Her - zen tief be - wegt
Sie drück - te mir die Hän - de Und ging dann schweigend fort.
Nie soll sie wie - der wei - nen Um mich vor Gram und Schmerz.

1. I stood beside my mother
   Who loves me without fail,
   But she was sad and silent
   For I had caused her pain.
   I placed my trembling fingers
   Upon her hands so kind,
   Was also sad and silent
   And troubled in my mind.

2. And as I stood beside her,
   A drop fell from her eye,
   A tear so hot and tender,
   It almost made me cry
   Then quickly rose my mother,
   Still silent as a tomb,
   She took my hands and squeezed them
   And then she left the room.

3. I understood her crying
   For quick was I to learn
   And deep down I appreciate
   Her love and her concern.
   Therefore, I will not trouble
   Her loving heart again,
   And never see her crying
   For me in grief and pain.

Des Menschen Glück, sein Sonnenschein, das ist die Liebe ganz allein!

160

Nun danket alle Gott

Now Thank We All Our God

1. Nun dan-ket al - le Gott mit Her - zen, Mund und Hän - den,
der gro - ße Din-ge tut an uns und al - len En - den,
2. Der e - wig rei-che Gott woll uns bei uns - rem Le - ben,
ein im - mer fröh-lich Herz' und ed - len Frie - den ge - ben,
3. Lob, Ehr und Preis sei Gott, dem Va - ter und dem Soh - ne,
und dem, der bei - den gleich im höch-sten Him - mels-thro - ne,

1. der uns von Mut - ter - leib und Kin - des - bei - nen an un-
2. und uns in sei - ner Gnad' er - hal - ten fort und fort und
3. dem ei - nig höch-sten Gott, als es an - fäng - lich war und

zäh - lig viel zu gut bis hier - her hat ge - tan.
uns aus al - ler Not er - lö - sen hier und und im - mer dort.
ist und blei - ben wird jetzt - und und im - mer dar.

1. Now thank we all our God with heart and hands and voices,
Who wondrous things hath done, in whom His world rejoices;
Who from our mother's arms hath blessed us on our way
With countless gifts of love, and still is ours today.

2. Oh, may this bounteous God thro' all our life be near us,
With ever joyful hearts and blessed peace to cheer us
And keep us in His grace and guide us when perplexed
And free us from all ills in this world and the next!

3. All praise and thanks to God the Father now be given,
The Son, and Him who reigns with them in highest heaven:
The one eternal God, whom earth and heav'n adore!
For thus it was, is now and shall be evermore. Amen.

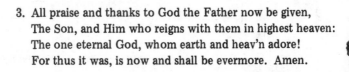

Wir pflügen und wir streuen

We Plow the Fields and Scatter

1. Wir pflü-gen und wir streu-en den Sa-men auf das Land,
2. Er sen-det Tau und Re-gen und Sonn und Mon-den-schein,
3. Was nah ist und was fer-ne von Gott kommt al-les her,

Doch Wachstum und Ge-dei-hen steht in des Him-mels Hand.
Er wick-elt sei-nen Se-gen gar zart und künst-lich ein
Der Strohhalm und die Ster-ne, das Sand-Korn und das Meer

Der tut mit lei-sem We-hen sich mild und heim-lich auf
Und bringt ihn dann be-hen-de in un-ser Feld und Brot.
Von ihm sind Büsch' und Blät-ter und Korn und Obst von ihm,

Und träuft wenn heim wir ge-hen Wuchs und Ge-dei-hen drauf.
Es geht durch uns-re Hän-de, kommt a-ber her von Gott.
Das schö-ne Früh-lings-wet-ter und Schnee und Un-ge-stüm.

Al - le gu - te Ga - be kommt her von Gott dem Herrn,

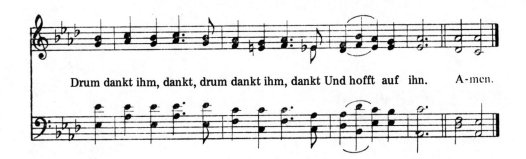

Drum dankt ihm, dankt, drum dankt ihm, dankt Und hofft auf ihn.   A-men.

1. We plow the fields and scatter
   The good seed on the land,
   But it is fed and watered
   By God's almighty hand;
   He sends the snow in winter,
   The warmth to swell the grain,
   The breezes and the sunshine,
   And soft, refreshing rain.

2. He only is the maker
   Of all things near and far,
   He paints the wayside flower,
   He lights the evening star;
   The winds and waves obey Him,
   By Him the birds are fed:
   Much more, to us His children,
   He gives our daily bread.

3. We thank Thee, then, O Father,
   For all things bright and good —
   The seedtime and the harvest,
   Our life, our health, our food;
   Accept the gifts we offer
   For all Thy love imparts,
   And, what Thou most desirest,
   Our humble, thankful hearts.

Chorus:

All good gifts around us
Are sent from heaven above:
Then thank the Lord, O thank the Lord
For all His love. Amen

A General Thanksgiving

Almighty God, Father of all mercies,
we your unworthy servants give you humble thanks
for all Your goodness and loving-kindness to us
and to all men.

We bless You for our creation, preservation,
and all the blessings of this life;
but above all for Your incomparable love
in the redemption of the world by our Lord Jesus Christ;
for the means of grace, and for the hope of glory.

And, we pray, give us such an awareness of Your mercies,
that with truly thankful hearts
we may make known Your praise,
not only with our lips, but in our lives,
by giving up ourselves to Your service,
and by walking before You in holiness and righteousness all our days;
through Jesus Christ our Lord,
to whom, with You and the Holy Spirit,
be all honor and glory throughout all ages.

Amen.

163

Alle Jahre wieder

As Each Happy Christmas

1. Al - le Jah - re wie - der kommt das Chri - stus - kind
2. Kehrt mit sei - nem Se - gen ein in je - des Haus,
3. Ist auch mir zur Sei - te still und un - er - kannt,

auf die Er - de nie - der, wo wir Men - schen sind.
geht auf al - len We - gen mit uns ein und aus.
daß es treu mich lei - te an der lie - ben Hand.

As each happy Christmas
Dawns on earth again,
Comes the holy Christ child
To the hearts of men.

Enters with his blessing
Into ev'ry home
Guides and guards our footsteps
As we go and come.

All unknown, beside me
He will ever stand,
And will safely lead me
With His own right hand.

Der schönste Baum

Oh, Christmas Tree

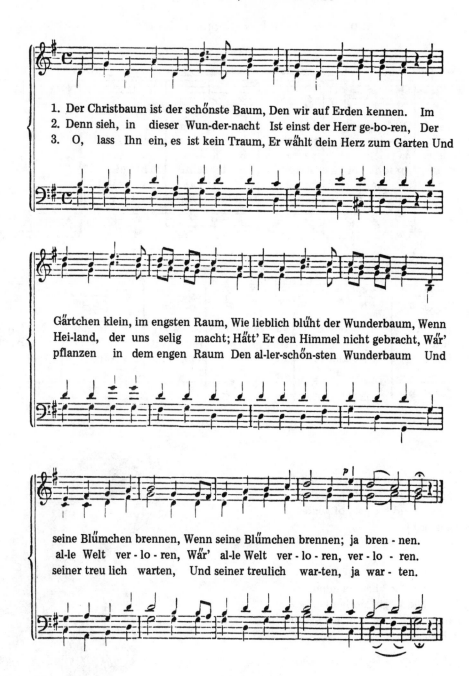

1. Der Christbaum ist der schönste Baum, Den wir auf Erden kennen. Im
2. Denn sieh, in   dieser Wun-der-nacht Ist einst der Herr ge-bo-ren, Der
3. O,   lass Ihn ein, es ist kein Traum, Er wählt dein Herz zum Garten Und

Gärtchen klein, im engsten Raum, Wie lieblich blüht der Wunderbaum, Wenn
Hei-land, der uns selig   macht; Hätt' Er den Himmel nicht gebracht, Wär'
pflanzen   in dem engen Raum Den al-ler-schön-sten Wunderbaum   Und

seine Blümchen brennen, Wenn seine Blümchen brennen; ja bren - nen.
al-le Welt ver - lo - ren, Wär' al-le Welt ver - lo - ren, ver - lo - ren.
seiner treu lich warten,   Und seiner treulich   war-ten, ja war - ten.

1. Oh, Christmas tree, you wonder tree
   On earth there is no other.
   In gardens small or mansions tall
   It's joyous message bring to all
   When all its lights are gleaming
   When all its lights are gleaming
   Yes, gleaming.

2. For once on this all blessed night
   The Lord God in his holy might
   Sent Jesus Christ, Saviour to be
   Bringing Peace to men on earth came He
   To save His world from sinning
   To save His world from sinning
   Yes, sinning.

3. It is no dream, just let him in
   He'll make your heart a garden
   Will plant there for eternity
   The loveliest of all Christmas trees.
   Then you shall bless Him ever.
   Then you shall bless Him ever.
   Yes, ever.

Es ist ein Ros' entsprungen

Lo, How a Rose E'er Blooming

1. {Es ist ein' Ros' ent-sprun-gen aus ei-ner Wur-zel zart,} und hat ein
   {wie uns die Al-ten sun-gen, von Jes-se kam die Art} Aus Got-tes

2. {Das Rös-lein, das ich mei-ne, da von Je-sa-ias sagt,} Wahr'Mensch und
   {hat uns ge-bracht al-leine Ma-rie, die reine Magd.}

3. {Das Blü-me-lein so klei-ne, das duf-tet uns so süß,}
   {mit sei-nem hel-len Schei-ne ver-treibts die Fin-ster-nis.}

Blüm-lein bracht mit-ten im kal-ten Win-ter, wohl zu der hal-ben Nacht.
ew'-gem Rat hat sie ein Kind ge-bo-ren wohl zu der hal-ben Nacht.
wah-rer Gott, hilft uns aus al-len Lei-den, ret-tet von Sünd und Tod.

1. Lo, how a rose e'er blooming From tender stem hath sprung,
   Of Jesse's lineage coming, As men of old have sung.
   It came a floweret bright, Amid the cold of winter
   When half spent was the night.

2. Isaiah 'twas foretold it, The rose I have in mind,
   With Mary we behold it, The Virgin Mother kind.
   To show God's love aright She bore to men a Savior,
   When half spent was the night.

Freue dich, Welt

Joy to the World

1. Freu - e dich Welt, der Herr er - schien, Der Kö - nig,
2. Freu - e dich Welt, dein Ret - ter kam Her - ab vom
3. Er kam, dass er der Welt zum Heil Des Va - ters

Je - sus Christ! Ein je - des Herz mach' Raum für ihn
Him - mels thron! Held, Frie - de - fürst, das ist sein Nam';
Wil - len tu'; Wer an ihn glaubt, dem wird zu - teil

Der al - ler Hei - land ist,   Der al - ler Hei - land
Des Va - ters ein 'ger Sohn.   Des Va - ters ein 'ger
Er - lö - sung, Fried' und Ruh,   Er - lö - sung, Fried' und

ist,   Der je - der - mann sein Heil - and ist.
Sohn.   Des Va - ters Ein - ge - born - er Sohn.
Ruh.   Er - lö - sung, Fried' und ew' ge Ruh'.

1. Joy to the world! The Lord is come;
   Let earth receive her King;
   Let every heart prepare Him room,
   And heaven and nature sing,
   And heaven and nature sing,
   And heaven, and heaven and nature sing.

2. Joy to the earth the Saviour reigns;
   Let men their songs employ;
   While fields and floods, rocks, hills and plains,
   Repeat the sounding joy,
   Repeat the sounding joy,
   Repeat, repeat the sounding joy.

3. He rules the world with truth and grace,
   And makes the nations prove
   The glories of His righteousness,
   And wonders of His love,
   And wonders of His love,
   And wonders, wonders of His love.

167

Morgen, Kinder, wird's was geben

What a Day Will Be Tomorrow

Mäßig

1. { Mor - gen, Kin - der, wird's was ge - ben, mor - gen wer - den wir uns freun!
   Welch ein Ju - bel, welch ein Le - ben wird in un - serm Hau - se sein!

2. { Wie wird dann die Stu - be glän - zen von der gro - ßen Lich - ter - zahl!
   Schö - ner als bei fro - hen Tän - zen ein ge - putz - ter Kro - nen - saal!

Ein - mal wer - den wir noch wach, hei - ßa, dann ist Weih - nachts - tag!
Wißt ihr noch vom vor' - gen Jahr, wie's am heil' - gen A - bend war?

3. Welch ein schöner Tag ist morgen!
   Viele Freude hoffen wir;
   Unsre lieben Eltern sorgen
   Lange, lange schon dafür.
   ǁ: O gewiss, wer sie nicht ehrt,
   Ist der ganzen Lust nicht wert. :ǁ

1. What a day will be tomorrow,
   Glad and happy we will be,
   Gone will be all fear and sorrow,
   All replaced by gaiety.
   One more night and we shall say,
   "Fa la la, it's Christmas Day."

2. All the candles brightly shining
   Filling our house with light.
   Feasts and dances all combining
   Can't compare with such a sight.
   Oh, I do remember fine
   How last year the room did shine.

3. Heav'nly day this blessed morning
   Many joys are ours to share.
   Our dear parents long preparing
   Making plans with loving care.
   Now inspired from heav'n above
   Show them honor, praise and love.

Zu Weihnachten
hörte man bei den Kleinen oft folgende Verse:

1. Pelzemärte, Knocha,
   Bet' ich alle Wocha,
   Bet ich bis ens Hemmelreich,
   Was ich krieg', des ess ich gleich.
   Pelzamärte, krommer Hond,
   Spreng' en onsrer Stub en d' Rond!

2. Christkendle komm' von draussa roi,
   Breng' mer schöne Sacha roi,
   Äpfel, Biera, Nussa,
   Mach' mer koi Verdrussa.

Ihr Kinderlein kommet

O Come Little Children

1. Ihr Kin-der-lein, kom-met, o kom-met doch all! Zur Krip-pe her
2. O seht in der Krip-pe im nächt-li-chen Stall, seht hier bei des

kom-met in Beth-le-hems Stall und seht, was in die-ser hoch-
Lich-tes hell-glän-zen-dem Strahl in rein-li-chen Win-deln das

hei-li-gen Nacht der Va-ter im Him-mel für Freu-de uns macht.
himm-li-sche Kind, viel schö-ner und hol-der, als En-gel es sind.

3. Da liegt es, das Kindlein, auf Heu und auf Stroh,
Maria und Joseph betrachten es froh,
Die redlichen Hirten knien betend davor,
Hoch oben schwebt jubelnd der Engelein Chor.

4. O beugt wie die Hirten anbetend die Knie,
Erhebet die Händlein und danket wie sie;
Stimmt freudig, ihr Kinder, wer wollt'sich nicht freun,
Stimmt freudig zum Jubel der Engel mit ein!

1. O come little children, O come one and all!
   O come to the cradle in Bethlehem's stall!
   And see what the Father, from high heav'n above,
   Has sent us tonight as proof of His love.

2. O see in the cradle this night in the stall,
   See here wondrous light that is dazzling to all,
   In clean lovely white lies the heavenly Child.
   Not even the angels are more sweet and mild.

3. O see where He's lying, the heavenly Boy!
   Here Joseph and Mary behold Him with joy;
   The shepherds have come, and are kneeling in pray'r,
   While songs of the angels float over Him there.

Kommet ihr Hirten

Come All You Shepherds

1. {Kom - met, ihr Hir - ten, ihr Män - ner und Fraun,
   kom - met, das lieb - li - che Kind - lein zu schaun!}

{Chri - stus der Herr ist heu - te ge - bo - ren,
den Gott zum Heiland euch hat er - ko - ren.} Fürchtet euch nicht!

2. Lasset uns sehen in Bethlehems Stall,
   was uns verheißen der himmlische Schall.
   Was wir dort finden,
   lasset uns künden,
   lasset uns preisen
   in frommen Weisen:
   Halleluja!

3. Wahrlich, die Engel verkündigen heut
   Bethlehems Hirtenvolk gar große Freud.
   Nun soll es werden
   Friede auf Erden,
   den Menschen allen
   ein Wohlgefallen.
   Ehre sei Gott!

1. Come all you shepherds, come quickly and see.
   The Christ Child from Heaven, with us now will be
   For Jesus our Lord this day has been born
   And came as our Saviour this world to adorn.
   Be not dismayed.

2. Let us then to Bethlehem go, there to view
   What has long been foretold by heavenly law.
   Let us then who seek and praising rejoice
   Telling to all now with heart and with voice.
   Hallelujah!

3. Angels today are joyfully telling abroad
   To shepherds the message as it was foretold
   Decreed was the time then for Peace here on earth!
   All mankind blest shall be and know its true worth.
   Praise be to God!

170

Herbei, o ihr Gläubigen

O Come All Ye Faithful

1. Her - bei, o ihr Gläu - bi - gen, fröh - lich tri - um - phie - rend, o
2. Du Kö - nig der Eh - ren, du Herr - scher der Heer - scha - ren, ver -

kom - met, o kom - met nach Beth - le - hem! Se - het das
schmähst nicht zu ruhn in Ma - ri - en Schoß, du wah - rer

Kind - lein, uns zum Heil ge - bo - ren! O las - set uns an - be - ten, o
Gott, von E - wig - keit ge - bo - ren! O las - set uns an - be - ten, o

las - set uns an - be - ten, o las - set uns an - be - ten den Kö - nig!
las - set uns an - be - ten, o las - set uns an - be - ten den Kö - nig!

3. Dir, der du bist heute ein Mensch für uns geboren,
O Jesu, sei Ehre und Preis und Ruhm,
Dir, Fleisch gewordnes Wort des ew'gen Vaters!
O lasset uns anbeten, o lasset uns anbeten,
O lasset uns anbeten den König.

1. O come, all ye faithful, Joyful and triumphant,
O come ye, O come ye to Bethlehem!
Come and behold Him, Born the King of angels!

Chorus:
O come, let us adore Him, O come, let us adore Him
O come, let us adore Him, Christ, the Lord!

2. O sing, choirs of angels, Sing in exultation!
O sing, all ye citizens of heaven above!
Glory to God, all Glory in the highest!

3. Yea, Lord, we greet Three, Born this happy morning,
O Jesus to Thee be all glory given;
Word of the Father, Now in flesh appearing!

O Tannenbaum!

What an important part of our festivities is the Christmas tree with its beautiful green branches, colored lights, decorations and gifts! Have you ever wondered where the custom originated?

The Christmas tree is of very early origin. In the ancient world, the Romans had a winter festival called Saturnalia which was held in honor of Saturn, their god of the seed-sowing. At these annual festivals it was customary to have trees laden with decorations and gifts. Vergil, the great Roman poet, mentions the tree with its swinging toys in one of his poems. During the Barbarian Invasions the Goths adopted the customs of the Saturnalia, including the tree custom, and brought them back into Germany.

The tree, however, did not become a part of the Christmas festivities until the time of Martin Luther. When once it was adopted as a Christian symbol, it became very popular throughout Germany. As a Christian symbol the tree, which is evergreen, represents Christ, Who is ever-living and eternally the same. Today, almost every home in Germany must have at least one tree. From Germany the Christmas tree custom spread into other lands, and is one of the most common symbols of Christmas.

The stirring melody of "O Tannenbaum!" is very familiar in America where several states have adopted it for their official state song. Best known of these is "Maryland, My Maryland".

In Germany this old folk-tune, with its traditional words, is rivaled only by the lovely "Stille Nacht" in popular favor.

O Tannenbaum

Oh Christmas Tree

1. O Tannenbaum, o Tannenbaum, wie treu sind deine Blätter! Du
2. O Tannenbaum, o Tannenbaum, du kannst mir sehr gefallen! Wie
3. O Tannenbaum, o Tannenbaum, dein Kleid will mich was lehren: Die

grünst nicht nur zur Sommerszeit, nein, auch im Winter, wenn es schneit. O
oft hat doch zur Weihnachtszeit ein Baum von dir mich hoch erfreut! O
Hoffnung und Beständigkeit gibt Trost und Kraft zu jeder Zeit. O

Tannenbaum, o Tannenbaum, wie treu sind deine Blätter!
Tannenbaum, o Tannenbaum, du kannst mir sehr gefallen.
Tannenbaum, o Tannenbaum, dein Kleid will mich was lehren.

1. O Tannenbaum, o Tannenbaum,
   Your leaves are ever faithful!
   Not only green when summer glows,
   But in the winter when it snows.
   O Tannenbaum, o Tannenbaum,
   Your leaves are ever faithful!

2. O Tannenbaum, o Tannenbaum,
   You are the tree most loved!
   How oft you've given me delight
   When Christmas fires were burning bright!
   O Tannenbaum, o Tannenbaum,
   You are the tree most loved!

3. O Tannenbaum, o Tannenbaum,
   Your faithful leaves will teach me
   That hope and love and constancy
   Give joy and peace eternally.
   O Tannenbaum, o Tannenbaum,
   Your faithful leaves will teach me!

Silent Night

On Christmas Eve, 1818, the organ of St. Nicholas Church, Oberndorf, Austria, was in need of repair. Oberndorf was snowbound, and there was no repairman for miles around. Yet there must be some form of special music for the Christmas service. Franz Gruber, church organist, lay the matter before his friend Joseph Mohr, vicar of the church, suggesting that a new song might be helpful in the emergency. At this suggestion Mohr wrote the lovely verses of "Stille Nacht" ("Silent Night"). Gruber immediately composed the music for it and presented the new song at the Christmas Midnight Mass. It was sung in a three-part arrangement to the accompaniment of a guitar.

When the organ repairman arrived from Tyrol, a few days later, Gruber showed him the new song. He was pleased with it and took it to a family in the Austrian Tyrol, who made extended concert tours and were famous for their singing of folk-songs. Through this family the song became known in Germany even before it was published.

In 1840, at Leipzig, it was printed as a "Tyrolean" Christmas song. In its travels about Germany the song had lost the names of its composers. It was thought to be a folk-song, and as such, no one suspected that the authorship could be determined. At one time the name of Michael Haydn (brother of the famous Franz Joseph) was associated with the song as its composer. It has since been learned that he made a four-part arrangement of it.

It is only recently that the true story of "Silent Night" has become generally known. The first inquiry into the origin of the song was made in 1854 by musicians of the royal court in Berlin. Later investigations by Ludvig Erk and H. E. Zimmerman have thrown much light on the subject. Zimmerman in "The Homiletic Review" tells us that "the same inspiration which moved the priest seized the organist". One might think that some divine inspiration alone could make it possible to compose the words and music of such an immortal song in but a few hours. From the little hamlet of Oberndorf in Austria, the song has found its way into every hamlet of the Christian World. Zimmerman says that it found its way across the ocean to America through a group of Tyrolean singers.

Wherever this exquisite carol is sung, it awakens precious memories of childhood, of lighted Christmas trees in darkened churches and homes. The very simplicity of the song and the tranquil beauty of its music seem to breathe the atmosphere of the humble manger-birth. It has sung its way into the hearts of mankind, being now one of the universal favorites, and has been translated into no less than ninety different languages and dialects.

Stille Nacht, heilige Nacht

Silent Night, Holy Night

1. Stil - le Nacht, hei - li - ge Nacht. Al - les schläft, ein - sam wacht
2. Stil - le Nacht, hei - li - ge Nacht. Hir - ten erst kund ge - macht,
3. Stil - le Nacht, hei - li - ge Nacht. Got - tes Sohn, o wie lacht

nur das trau - te, hoch - hei - li - ge Paar. Hol - der Kna - be in lok - ki-gem Haar,
durch der En - gel Hal - le - lu - ja tönt es laut von fern und nah':
Lieb' aus dei - nem gött - li-chen Mund, da uns schlägt die ret - ten-de Stund',

schlaf in himm - li - scher Ruh', schlaf in himm - li-scher Ruh'.
Christ der Ret - ter, ist da, Christ der Ret - ter, ist da.
Christ in dei - ner Ge - burt, Christ in dei - ner Ge - burt.

1. Silent night! holy night! All is calm! All is bright!
Round yon Virgin, Mother and Child
Holy infant so tender and mild
Sleep in heavenly peace, sleep in heavenly peace.

2. Silent night! holy night! Shepherds quake at the sight,
Glories stream from heaven afar,
Heavenly hosts sing: "Alleluia;
Christ the Saviour is born, Christ the Saviour is born.

3. Silent night! holy night! Son of God, love's pure Light
Radiant beams from Thy holy face,
With the dawn of redeeming grace,
Jesus, Lord, at Thy birth, Jesus Lord, at Thy birth.

O du fröhliche

1. O du fröh-li-che, o du se-li-ge, gna-den-brin-gen-de Weih-nachts-zeit! Welt ging ver-lo-ren, Christ ward ge-bo-ren: Freu-e, freu-e dich, o Chri-sten-heit!

2. O du fröh-li-che, o du se-li-ge, gna-den-brin-gen-de Weih-nachts-zeit! Christ ist er-schie-nen, uns zu ver-süh-nen: Freu-e, freu-e dich, o Chri-sten-heit!

3. O du fröh-li-che, o du se-li-ge, gna-den-brin-gen-de Weih-nachts-zeit! Himm-li-sche Hee-re jauch-zen dir Eh-re: Freu-e, freu-e dich, o Chri-sten-heit!

Süsser die Glocken nie klingen

Sweeter the Bells Never Ring

1. Süs-ser die Glocken nie klin-gen, Als zu der Weihnachtszeit;
2. O wenn die Glocken er-klin-gen, Schnell sie das Christkindlein hört,
3. Klin-get mit lieb-li-chem Schal-le U-ber die Meere noch weit,

'sist als ob En-ge-lein sin-gen Wie-der von Frie-den und Freud',
Tut sich vom Himmel dan schwingen, Ei-let her-nie-der zur Erd',
Dass sich er-freu-en doch al-le Sei-li-ger Weih-nachts-zeit.

Wie sie ge-sun-gen in se-li-ger Nacht, Wie sie ge-sun-gen in
Seg-net den Va-ter, die Mut-ter, das Kind, Segnet den Va-ter, die
Al-le auf-jauch-zen mit ei-nem Ge-sang, Al-le auf-jauchzen mit

se-li-ger Nacht.
Mutter, das Kind. } Glocken mit heiligem Klang, Klingt doch die Erde entlang!
ei-nem Ge-sang.

1. Sweeter are bells never ringing
   Than Christmas time, all o'r the earth.
   T'is as if angels are singing
   The story of heavenly birth,
   ‖: Just as they did on that holy night. :‖
   Ring out, oh bells, far and wide
   Bringing joy this Christmas tide.

2. Sounds of the bells now are sending
   Heavenward our concerns.
   Swiftly from heaven descending,
   Gladly the Christ Child returns,
   ‖: Blessing the father, the mother, the child. :‖
   Ring out, oh bells, far and wide
   Bringing joy this Christmas tide.

3. Ring with joy from every steeple
   Far across oceans and glen,
   Spreading good news to all people,
   Peace and good will to all men,
   ‖: All now rejoice and sing out in accord. :‖
   Ring out, oh bells, far and wide
   Bringing joy this Christmas tide.

From Heaven Above

Early Christmas Eve (1534), in order to lighten the many household duties for his wife, Martin Luther sits beside the cradle of his little son, Paul. He has been studying the Christmas Gospel in preparation for the festive services. He is deep in thought. Suddenly he becomes aware of the figure of the little child before him in the cradle. It is Paul—how like the child Jesus lying in the manger! His heart swells with emotion. He takes down his lute and begins to hum and sing. He happens upon the popular folk song "Aus Fremden Landen Komm Ich Her" ("From Foreign Lands I Come Here"). Using this as his pattern, he continues to sing to little Paul about the Christmas story, adding verse after verse. He writes and revises the verses. Finally there are fifteen in all, and a new Christmas song for children has been composed.

By nature Luther was deeply moved by the Christmas spirit. Especially did he love to join the children in celebrating Christmas. Special festivities were held for the children at Luther's home on Christmas Eve. At these annual festivities "From Heaven Above To Earth I Come" was one of the children's favorite songs. In singing the song, it was Luther's custom to have a student, dressed as an angel, sing the first seven verses. The children would then joyfully respond by singing the remaining verses, and on the last verse would leap about in a gleeful dance.

"From Heaven Above" was first published in Wittenberg, in 1535. In 1543, it was included in "Klug's Hymnbook" with the subtitle, "A Children's Hymn of the Christ Child for Christmas Eve". The hymn is still sung from the dome of the Kreuz Church, in Dresden, before daybreak Christmas Morning.

Luther was a great lover of music and urged that all learn to enjoy it. As a boy, he had sung carols in the streets of Magdeburg. During his lifetime, he wrote, revised and translated many hymns. Of these, none is more touching in its simplicity and directness than this Christmas song.

"Music," said Luther, "is a gift of God. It makes people cheerful. I give music the highest and most honorable place."

Vom Himmel hoch da komm ich her

From Heaven on High

1. Vom Him-mel hoch da komm ich her, ich bring euch gu-te, neu-e Mär;
2. Euch ist ein Kindlein heut ge-born von ei-ner Jungfrau aus-er-kor'n;
3. Es ist der HerrChrist,un-ser Gott, der will euch führn aus al-ler Not;

der gu-ten Mär bring ich so viel, da-von ich sing'n und sa-gen will.
ein Kin-de-lein so zart und fein, das soll eu'r Freud und Won-ne sein.
er will eu'r Hei-land sel-ber sein, von al-len Sün-den ma-chen rein.

4. Er bringt euch alle Seligkeit,
Die Gott der Vater hat bereit,
Daß ihr mit uns im Himmelreich
Sollt leben nun und ewiglich.

5. Des laßt uns alle fröhlich sein
Und mit den Hirten gehn hinein,
Zu sehn, was Gott uns hat beschert,
Mit seinem lieben Sohn verehrt.

6. Lob, Ehr sei Gott im höchsten Thron,
Der uns schenkt seinen eingen Sohn;
Des freuen sich der Engel Schar
Und singen uns solch's neues Jahr.

1. From heaven on high I come to earth
To tell you of the Savior's birth.
Good news I bring for all to hear,
This is my message of good cheer.

2. To you, this day, is born a child,
Born by a virgin, pure and mild.
A child so tender and so sweet
To be your peace and joy indeed.

3. God's only son, the Christ, is he,
Will lead you out of misery.
To cleanse you from iniquity
Your savior he has come to be.

4. Just like the shepherds let us run
To see what God sent in His son.
He sent his love and set us free.
Rejoice and thank Him joyfully.

Kinder-Lieder

Backe, backe Kuchen

Bake, Bake a Cake

Bak-ke, bak-ke Ku-chen, der Bäk-ker hat ge-ru-fen! Wer will gu-ten Ku-chen bak-ken, der muß ha-ben sie-ben Sa-chen: Ei-er und Schmalz, But-ter und Salz, Milch und Mehl, Sa-fran macht den Ku-chen gel. Schieb, schieb in O-fen rein!

"Cakes, fresh cakes, I say"
The baker's calling out today.
He who wants to bake a cake,
Seven things he has to take:
Eggs and lard, butter and salt,
Milk and flour. Saffron makes it
nice and yellow.
Into the oven, quick!

Wenn die Kindlein unruhig wurden, nahm man sie aufs
Knie und sang ihnen Folgendes vor:

1. Backe, backe Kuchen
   Der Bäcker hat gerufen,
   Wer will gute Kuchen backen,
   Der muss haben sieben Sachen:
   Eier und Schmalz,
   Butter und Salz,
   Milch und Mehl,
   Safran macht den Kuchen gel (gelb).

2. Backe, backe Kucha,
   Der Bäcker hat gerufa,
   Hat gerufa die ganze Nacht;
   's Kend kriegt keinen Teig gemacht,
   Kriegt auch keinen Kuchen,
   Kriegt auch keinen Kuchen.

3. Patsche, patsche Kucha,
   Der Bäcker hat gerufa,
   Weisse Schüla, schwarze Strümpfla,
   Morga kann ich tanza.

Der Butzemann

The Bogyman

1. Es tanzt ein Bi - Ba - But - ze - mann in un - serm Haus her - um, bi - de - bum, es tanzt ein Bi - Ba - But - ze - mann in un - serm Haus her - um. Er rüt - telt sich, er schüt - telt sich, er wirft sein Säck - lein hin - ter sich. Es tanzt ein Bi - ba - But - ze - mann in un - serm Haus her - um.

2. Es tanzt ein Bi - Ba - Butzemann
In unserm Haus herum, bidebum
Es tanzt ein Bi - Ba - Butzemann
In unserm Haus herum
Er wirft sein Säcklein her und hin,
Was ist wohl in dem Säcklein drin?
Es tanzt ein Bi - Ba - Butzemann
In unserm Haus herum.

3. Es tanzt ein Bi - Ba - Butzemann
In unserm Haus herum, bidebum
Es tanzt ein Bi - Ba - Butzemann
In unserm Haus herum
Er bringt zur Nacht dem guten Kind
Die Äpfel, die im Säcklein sind.
Es tanzt ein Bi - Ba - Butzemann
In unserm Haus herum.

4. Es tanzt ein Bi - Ba - Butzemann
In unserm Haus herum, bidebum
Es tanzt ein Bi - Ba - Butzemann
In unserm Haus herum
Er wirft sein Säcklein hin und her,
Am Morgen ist es wieder leer.
Es tanzt ein Bi - Ba - Butzemann
In unserm Haus herum.

1. A little Be - Ba - Bogyman
   Is dancing round and round the house,
   A little Be - Ba - Bogyman
   Is dancing round the house.
   He shakes himself and jumps about,
   He flings his bag and gives a shout.
   A little Be - Ba - Bogyman
   Is dancing round the house.

2. A little Be - Ba - Bogyman
   Is dancing round and round the house,
   A little Be - Ba - Bogyman
   Is dancing round the house.
   His little bag swings fro and back,
   What could be hidden in his sack?
   A little Be - Ba - Bogyman
   Is dancing round the house.

3. A little Be - Ba - Bogyman
   Is dancing round and round the house,
   A little Be - Ba - Bogyman
   Is dancing round the house.
   At night he brings to children nice,
   The apples, sweet as sugar and spice.
   A little Be - Ba - Bogyman
   Is dancing round the house.

4. A little Be - Ba - Bogyman
   Is dancing round and round the house,
   A little Be - Ba - Bogyman
   Is dancing round the house.
   He throws around his little sack,
   By morning it's an empty bag.
   A little Be - Ba - Bogyman
   Is dancing round the house.

Grün, grün, grün

Green, Green, Green

Grün, grün, grün, sind al - le mei - ne Klei - der,

Grün, grün, grün liebt je - der - man. Dar - um lieb' ich

al - les was so grün ist, Denn mein Lieb ein Jä - ger ist.

Blau, blau, blau sind alle meine Kleider,
Blau, blau, blau liebt jederman.
Darum lieb' ich alles was so blau ist,
Denn mein Lieb ein Matrose ist.

Weiss, weiss, weiss sind alle meine Kleider,
Weiss, weiss, weiss liebt jederman.
Darum lieb' ich alles was so weiss ist,
Denn mein Lieb ein Bäcker ist.

Schwarz, schwarz, schwarz sind alle meine Kleider,
Schwarz, schwarz, schwarz liebt jederman.
Darum lieb' ich alles was so schwarz ist,
Denn mein Lieb ein Schornsteinfeger ist.

1. Green, green, green are all my pretty gowns,
   Green, green, green pleases ev'ryone.
   Therefore green is everything that I love
   For a hunter is my love.

2. Blue, blue, blue are all my pretty gowns,
   Blue, blue, blue pleases ev'ryone.
   Therefore blue is everything that I love
   For a sailor is my love.

3. White, white, white are all my pretty gowns,
   White, white, white pleases ev'ryone.
   Therefore white is everything that I love
   For a baker is my love.

4. Black, black, black are all my pretty gowns,
   Black, black, black pleases ev'ryone.
   Therefore black is everything that I love
   For a chimneysweep is my love.

183

Der Kuckuck und der Esel

The Cuckoo and the Donkey

1. Der Kuk - kuck und der E - sel, die
hat - ten ei - nen Streit, wer wohl am be - sten
sän - ge. wer wohl am be - sten sän - ge zur
schö-nen Mai - en - zeit, zur schö-nen Mai - en - zeit.

2. Der Kuckuck sprach: "Das kan ich!"
und hub gleich an zu schrein.
||: "Ich aber kann es besser!" :||
||: fiel gleich der Esel ein. :||

3. Das klang so schön und lieblich,
so schön von fern und nah
||: sie sangen alle beide :||
||: Kuckuck, Kuckuck, i-a! :||

1. The cuckoo and the donkey
they had a friendly fray:
who does the better singing :||
in this great month of May? :||

2. The cuckoo said: it's I
and started with a shout.
But I can do it better :||
the donkey joined the bout. :||

3. This was so nice and lively,
so joyful near and far
Together they kept singing :||
cuckoo, cuckoo, ee - ah :||

Hänschen klein

Little Johnny

1. Häns-chen klein ging al - lein in die wei - te Welt hin-ein,

Stock und Hut steht ihm gut, ist ganz wohl-ge - mut

a - ber Mut - ter wei - net sehr, hat ja nun kein

Häns-chen mehr. Wünsch' dir Glück, sagt ihr Blick, kehr nur bald zu-rück!

2. Sieben Jahr, trüb und klar, Hänschen in der Fremde war;
   da besinnt sich das Kind, eilet heim geschwind.
   Doch nun ist's kein Hänschen mehr, nein, ein gross Hans ist er,
   Stirn und Hand braun gebrannt, wird er wohl erkannt?

3. Eins, zwei, drei geh'n vorbei, wissen nicht, wer das wohl sei.
   Schwester spricht:"Welch Gesicht", kennt den Bruder nicht.
   Kommt daher die Mutter sein; schaut ihm kaum ins Aug' hinein,
   ruft sie schon: "Hans, mein Sohn! Grüss dich Gott, mein Sohn!"

1. Little John all alone wandered off the world to roam.
   Cane and hat suit him that he is really glad.
   But his mother weeps and cries,
   Johnny from her nest now flies.
   Wish you well her eyes tell, come back soon, farewell!

2. Seven years, joys and fears, to Johnny now a thought appears
   Why should I longer roam? I will hurry home.
   Little Johnny he's no more, big John, barely clears the door;
   Face and hand golden tanned, will they know this man?

3. Here and there everywhere walking by the girls so fair,
   Sister says, "Who is this?" How could she have missed.
   But when mother comes to view
   Looks into his eyes so blue,
   Shouts with joy, John my son, God be praised, my son.

Hoppe, hoppe Reiter

Hop, Hop Rider

Hoppe, hoppe Reiter,
Fällt er hin, so schreit er,
Fällt er von dem Pferde,
Liegt er auf der Erde;
Fällt er in das grüne Gras,
Macht er sich sein Pelzchen nass;
Fällt er in den Sumpf,
Macht der Reiter plumps!

When someone sat and bounced
a child on his knee, this song or
rhyme was sung or spoken.
There are many different varia-
tions of this ditty.

Bessarabien:

Hoppa, hoppa reita,
Müller (Vatter) schlacht a Säule,
Müller schlacht a rote Kuh,
Derf der Kleine au derzu?
Nein, nein, die stosst dich weg,
On no fliegscht en der Dreck!

Friedensfeld:

Hoppa, hoppa reita,
Dr Schemmel steht uf d' Seita,
Dr Vatter geht ens Wirtshaus,
Sauft alle Gläser aus,
Rums, do liegt er dronta!

Arzis:

Hoppa, hoppa Rössle,
Droba steht a Schlössle,
Droba steht en Kuckuckskaschta,
Gucken drei Madama raus,
Die eine spennt Seide,
Die andre spennt d' Weide,
Die dritt spennt en rota Rock
Für dr kleine Zottelbock.

U. W. Schwäbisch (Württemberg)

Trips, traps, drill,
Dr Bauer hat a Füll;
Das Füll, das will net laufa,
Dr Bauer will's verkaufa;
Nu lauft's em Bauer weg,
No hat dr Bauer en Dreck.

Hoppa, hoppa reita,
Fällt er na, no schreit er,
Steht er wieder uff,
Hockt sich oba nuff.

Beresina:

Hoppa, hoppa reita,
Säbel an der Seita,
's Geld en der Tascha,
Der Woi en de Flascha,
Hoch droba uf der Mauer
Sen die Apfel süss on sauer.

Hoppa, hoppa reita,
Säbel an d'r Seita,
's Geld en de Tascha,
Bier en de Flascha.
Hoppst d'r Schemmel über'n Graba,
Fallt er ronter, muss er saga:
Plimps, plumps, liegt er drin!

Hoppa hoppa reita,
Säbel an der Seita,
's Brod liegt dernebed,
Moi Mutter ischt a gute Frau,
Was se kocht, des ess ich au,
No keine kloine Stoi.

Hoppa, hoppa Rössle
Droba steht a Schlössle,
Droba steht a goldigs Haus,
Gucket drei Madama raus,
Eine spennet Seide,
Die andere wickelt Weide,
Die dritte spennt en rota Rock
Fur ihren kloina Zottelbock.

Welzheim

Hoppa, hoppa Gäule,
Dr Müller sticht a Säule,
Dr Müller sticht a roate Kuah,
's Bluet lauft dr Kuche zue,
Mueder, lass mi an drzua,
Oder Gang i net en d' Schuel.
Schnaps liegt er d' onta!

Gnadental:

Hoppa, hoppa reita,
Sabel in der Seita,
Sabel in der rechta Hand,
Treibt die Russa aus dem Land.

Offizier von Papier,
Juchha, juchha, rombalier!
Läus uf em Kopf,
Wie en Knopf,
Läus en de Hosa,
Wie Franzosa.

Hoppa, hoppa Reiter,
Wenn er fällt, no schreit er,
Fällt er in den Graben,
Fressen ihn die Raben,
Fällt er in den Sumpf,
Macht er einen Plumps.

Allegmein:

Hopp, hopp, hopp,
Pferdchen, lauf Galopp,
Über Stock und über Steine,
Aber brich dir nicht die Beine,
Hopp, hopp, hopp,
Pferdchen, lauf Galopp!

Im Märzen

In March

1. Im Mär-zen der Bau-er die Röß-lein ein - spannt, er pflü-get den
er setzt sei - ne Fel-der und Wie-sen in Stand,

Bo- den, er eg-get und sät und rührt sei - ne Hän-de früh - mor-gens und spät.

2. Die Bäurin, die Mägde, sie dürfen nicht ruhn,
Sie haben im Haus und im Garten zu tun:
Sie graben und rechen und singen ein Lied,
Sie freun sich, wenn alles schön grünet und blüht.

3. So geht unter Arbeit das Frühjahr vorbei,
Da erntet der Bauer das duftende Heu;
Er mäht das Getreide, dann drischt er es aus;
Im Winter, da gibt es manch fröhlichen Schmaus.

1. When March comes, the farmer and horses prepare
   To work all the land which is under his care.
   He ploughs and he harrows and plants all his seeds,
   His hands always busy to work for our needs.

2. His wife and the maids don't have much time to sleep.
   There's work in the house, and a garden to keep.
   They're digging and raking, and singing at last
   When everything's blooming and growing so fast.

3. So springtime is fleeting while working away.
   The farmer is cutting the sweet-smelling hay.
   He harvests the grain and he threshes the wheat.
   When winter comes, all then may heartily eat.

188

Kuckuck, Kuckuck

Cuckoo, Cuckoo

1. Kuk - kuck, Kuk - kuck ruft aus dem Wald.

Las - set uns sin - gen, tan - zen und sprin - gen!

Früh - ling, Früh - ling wird es nun bald!

2. Kuckuck, Kuckuck lässt·nicht sein Schrein:
   "Komm in die Felder, Wiesen und Wälder!
   Frühling, Frühling, stelle dich ein!"

3. Kuckuck, Kuckuck, trefflicher Held!
   Was du gesungen, ist dir gelungen:
   Winter, Winter räumet das Feld.

1. Cuckoo, cuckoo, echoes his call.
   Now let's be dancing, singing and prancing,
   Springtime, springtime soon for us all.

3. Cuckoo, cuckoo, champion of spring!
   What you foretold is here to enfold us.
   Winter, winter, had it's last fling.

2. Cuckoo, cuckoo never keeps still,
   Flies through the meadows and forest shadows.
   Springtime, springtime, come, if you will.

Kuk-kuck, sag mir doch, wie-viel Jah - re leb ich noch?

(Nursery rhyme)

Cuckoo, tell me quick, how many years I shall live,
(A child asks, then counts the cuckoo's calls.)

Müde bin ich, geh' zur Ruh'

Weary Am I, to Rest Must Go

1. Mü - de bin ich, geh' zur Ruh', Schliesse mei - ne Au-gen zu;
2. Hab' ich Unrecht heut' ge - tan, Sieh' es, lie - ber Gott, nicht an;
3. Al - le, die mir sind verwandt, Gott, lass ruh'n in Dei-ner Hand;
4. Kranken Herzen sen - de Ruh', Nas - se Au - gen schliesse zu;

1. Va - ter, lass die Au - gen Dein Ü - ber meinem Bet - te sein.
2. Dei - ne Gnad' und Je - su Blut, Ma - che al - len Schaden gut.
3. Al - le Menschen, gross und klein, Sol - len Dir be - foh - len sein!
4. Lass in Dei - ner En - gel Wacht Sanft uns ru - hen die - se Nacht!

Note: These words are often used as a child's prayer.

1. Weary am I, to rest must go;
   My eyelids close as well I know
   Dear Father, that those eyes of Thine
   Fondly, will bless this bed of mine.

2. Have I done some wrong today
   Dear Lord, for your grace I pray.
   For Thy Love and Jesus' blood
   Every error shall make good.

3. Grant the heartsick tender rest,
   May their sorrowing eyes be blest.
   Let your Angel's watch this night
   Bring restful sleep 'til morning Light.

4. Send rest to the heartsick here
   Close your eyes with loving cheer
   Let your heavenly angel light
   Give us rest this blessed night.

Beim Anfang der Schule

O Herr, unser Gott, sei uns gnädig, segne uns bei unserm
Lernen und mach uns fromm und gehorsam durch deinen heiligen
Geist, damit wir deinen Namen ehren, dein Reich mehren und
deinen Willen tun. Durch Jesum Christum. Amen.

Sandmännchen

The Sandman

1. Die Blü - me-lein, sie schla - fen schon längst im Mon-den-schein, sie
2. Die Vö - ge-lein, sie san - gen so süß im Son-nen-schein, sind
3. Sand-männ chenkommt ge - schli - chen und guckt durchs Fen-ster - lein, ob
4. Sand-männ-chen aus dem Zim - mer! Es schläft mein Herz-chen fein, hat

nik - ken mit den Köpf - chen auf ih - ren Sten-ge - lein. Es
nun zur Ruh ge - gan - gen in ih - re Nest-chen klein; das
ir - gend noch ein Lieb - chen nicht mag zu Bet - te sein, und
schon gar fest ver - schlos - sen sein lieb Guck-äu - ge - lein. Es

schüt-telt sich der Blü - ten-baum, er säu-selt wie im Traum:
Heim-chen in dem Äh - ren-grund, es tut al - lein sich kund.
wo es nur ein Kind-lein fand, streut es ins Aug' ihm Sand.
leuch-tet mor-gen mir Will-komm', das Äu - ge-lein so fromm.

1.-4. Schla - fe, schla - fe, schlaf du, mein Kin - de - lein!

1. The flowers now to rest must go
   As the moon begins to shine
   Nodding little heads just so
   Upon each stem so fine.
   ‖: Then rustles ev'ry blooming tree
   And sighs as in a dream.
   Sleep now, sleep now, sleep now,
   Sleep, my baby, sleep. :‖

2. The birds that sang so sweetly
   By day, have gone to rest,
   And each is tucked up neatly
   All in its little nest;
   ‖: The cricket in the garden here
   Is still awake, I fear.
   Sleepy, sleepy, sleepy,
   Sleepy, baby mine.:‖

3. The Sandman will be coming
   And poking in his head,
   To look for naughty children
   That haven't gone to bed;
   ‖: And if he takes them by surprise,
   The sand flies in their eyes!
   Sleepy, sleepy, sleepy,
   Sleep, my baby, sleep,:‖

Schlaf, Herzenssöhnchen

Cradle Song

1. Schlaf, Her-zens-söhn-chen, mein Lieb-ling bist du! Schlie-sse die blau-en Guck-äu-ge-lein zu! Al-les ist ru-hig, ist still wie im Grab, schlaf nur, ich weh-re die Flie-gen dir ab.

2. Jetzt noch mein Püpp-chen, ist gol-de-ne Zeit, spä-ter, ach, spä-ter ist's nim-mer wie heut. Stel-len erst Sor-gen ums La-ger sich her, schläft sich's so ru-hig dir nicht mehr.

3. En-gel vom Him-mel, so lieb-lich wie du, schwe-ben ums Bett-chen und lä-cheln dir zu. Spä-ter zwar stei-gen sie spät auch und früh a-ber sie trock-nen nur Trä-nen dir ab.

4. Schlaf lie-bes Söhn-chen, und kommt gleich die Nacht, sitzt dei-ne Mut-ter am Bett-chen und wacht. Sei es so spät auch und sei es so früh Mut-ter-lieb, Herz-chen, ent schlummert doch nie.

1. Sleep, my own baby, my darling thou art;
Close thy blue eyes now, thou joy of my heart!
All is as quiet as quiet can be,
Never a fly shall alight upon thee.

2. Angels from heaven, as lovely as thou,
Hover around thee, and smile on thee now.
What if the angels must go by and by?
Yet when thou weepest, thy tears they will dry.

3. Gold are the hours that are gliding away,
Dear one, tomorrow is never today;
Come to thy bedside will sorrow and pain,
Ne're will thou slumber so sweetly again.

4. Sleep then, my baby, the dark do not fear,
Mother is sitting, and guarding thee here;
Darling, though late or though early it be,
Mother will never grow weary for thee.

Schlaf, Kindlein, schlaf

Sleep, Baby, Sleep

Schlaf, Kindlein, schlaf! Der Vater hüt' die Schaf', die Mutter schüttelt

'sBäu-me-lein, da fällt her-ab ein Träu-me-lein. Schlaf, Kindlein, schlaf!

2. Schlaf, Kindlein, schlaf!
Am Himmel zieh'n die Schaf'!
Die Sternlein sind die Lämmerlein,
der Mond, der ist das Schäferlein.
Schlaf, Kindlein, schlaf!

3. Schlaf, Kindlein, schlaf!
So schenk ich dir ein Schaf
mit einer gold'nen Schelle fein,
das soll dein Spielgeselle sein.
Schlaf, Kindlein, schlaf!

1. Sleep, Baby, sleep
Your father herds the sheep
Your mother shakes the tree so small
And from it a sweet dream does fall
Sleep, Baby, Sleep.

2. Sleep, Baby, Sleep
White clouds shall be the sheep
The lambs from twinkling stars do peep
The moon as shepherd watch does keep
Sleep, Baby, Sleep.

3. Sleep, Baby, Sleep
This lamb is yours to keep
Its golden fleece so soft and fine
T'will be your love as you are mine
Sleep, Baby, Sleep.

Abendgebet

Müde bin ich, geh' zur Ruh,
schliesse beide Äuglein zu.
Vater, lass die Augen dein
über meinem Bette sein. Amen.

Kindergebete

1. Ich bin klein,
Mein Herz ist rein,
Soll niemand drin wohnen
Als Jesus allein!

2. Engele komm',
Mach' mich fromm,
Dass ich zu Dir in den Himmel komm!

3. Abba, lieber Vater, Amen!

Still, still, still

Peace, Peace, Peace

Fließend

Volksweise aus dem Salzburgischen, 1865

1. Still, still, still, weil's Kindlein schlafen will! Ma - ri - a tut es nie-der-sin-gen,

p dolce

ih - re keusche Brust darbringen, Still, still, still, weil's Kindlein schlafen will!

pp

2. Gross, gross, gross,
   die Lieb ist übergross!
   Gott hat den Himmelsthron verlassen
   und muss reisen auf den Strassen.
   Gross, gross, gross,
   die Lieb ist übergross!

3. Wir, wir, wir
   tun rufen all zu dir:
   "Tue uns des Himmels Reich aufschliessen,
   wenn wir einmal sterben müssen!"
   Wir, wir, wir,
   tun rufen all zu dir.

1. Still, still, still,
   The dear Baby lies asleep
   Mary a lullaby is singing
   A Mother's love so sweetly bringing
   Peace, Peace, Peace,
   The dear Baby lies asleep.

2. Great, great, great,
   The love of God is great!
   He left His glory throne on high
   With us on earth here to abide.
   Great, great, great,
   The love of God is great.

3. We, we, we,
   We call on high to Thee!
   Unlock for us the gates of heaven,
   For to Thee all power is given.
   We, we, we,
   We call on high to Thee!

Der gute Hirte

Weil ich Jesu Schäflein bin,
freu' ich mich nur immerhin
über meinen guten Hirten,
der mich wohl weiss zu bewirten,
der mich liebet, der mich kennt
und bei meinem Namen nennt.

Summ, summ, summ

Hum - Dum - Dee

1.-3. Summ, summ, summ, Bien-chen summ her-um!

1. Ei, wir tun dir nichts zu lei - de, flieg nur aus in
2. Son - ne ü - ber al - len We - gen, Blü - ten-duft weht
3. Füll mit sü - ßem Saft die Wa - ben, wol - len uns mit

Wald und Hei-de!
dir ent-ge-gen. } Summ, summ, summ, Bienchen summ her-um!
Ho-nig la-ben.

1. Hum — dum — dee, little honey bee.
We won't hurt you, friend of ours,
Fly around to all the flowers
Hum — dum — dee, little honey bee.

2. Hum — dum — dee, little honey bee.
Lovely sunshine, bright and fair,
Sweetest fragrance fills the air
Hum — dum — dee, little honey bee.

3. Hum — dum — dee, little honey bee.
Pollen gather without money
Love to eat your yummy honey
Hum — dum — dee, little honey bee.

Es fuhr ein Bauer ins Heu

"Sung To The Tune Of The Farmer In The Dell"

1. Es fuhr ein Bauer ins Heu,
   Es fuhr ein Bauer ins Heu,
   Schi, scha schöne Heu,
   Es fuhr ein Bauer ins Heu.

2. Der Bauer nahm sich ein Weib . . .
3. Das Weib nahm sich ein Kind . . .
4. Das Kind nahm sich eine Amm' . . .
5. Die Amm' nahm sich eine Magd . . .
6. Die Magd nahm sich ein'n Knecht . . .
7. Der Knecht verliess die Magd . . .
8. Die Magd verliess ihre Amm' . . .
9. Die Amm' verliess ihr Kind . . .
10. Das Kind verliess das Weib . . .
11. Das Weib verliess den Bauern . . .

195

Tanz, Kindlein, tanz

Dance, Child, Dance

Tanz, Kind - lein, tanz! Die
Schu - he sind noch ganz.
Lass dich nicht ge - reu - e, der
Schu - ster macht dir neu - e.
Tanz, Kind - lein, tanz!

Dance, dear child, dance
Your slippers are still new
Don't worry now, tis true
The cobbler will make them new
Dance, dear child, dance.

Wenn's den Kleinen irgendwo schmerzt, sagt man ihnen:

Heila, heila Sega,
Drei Tag Rega,
Drei Tag Schnee,
Morga früh tut's nemme weh!

Heila, heila, Sega,
Drei Tag Rega,
Drei Tag Kälberdreck,
Morga früh ischt alles weg.

Heila, heila Sega,
Drei Tag Rega,
Drei Tag Katzadreck,
Morga früh ischt alles weg!

Heila, heila, Sega
Drei Tag Rega,
Drei Tag blasst der Wind
Und heilt dem Kind
Sein Wehle g'schwind.

Fingerspiel

Des ischt der Dauma,
Der schüttelt Pflauma,
Der lest se uf,
Der tragt se nuf
On der Kloi
Freszt se alle uf.

Trarira! Der Sommer der ist da

Trarirum! The Summer Now Has Come

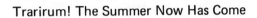

Tra - ri - ra! Der Sommer der ist da! Wir woll'n hinaus in'n Gar - ten Und

woll'n des Sommers war - ten. Ja, ja, ja, der Sommer der ist da.

Trarirum, the summer now has come!
We're running to the garden fast,
Hope summer will forever last.
Trarirum, the summer now has come!

Weisst du, wieviel Sternlein stehen?

Do You Know How Many Stars?

1. Weißt du, wie-viel Stern-lein ste-hen an dem blau-en Him-mels-zelt?
Weißt du, wie-viel Wol-ken ge-hen weit-hin ü-ber al-le Welt?
2. Weißt du wie-viel Mück-lein spie-len in der hel-len Son-nen-glut,
wie-viel Fisch-lein auch sich küh-len in der hel-len Was-ser-flut?
3. Weißt du, wie-viel Kin-der frü-he stehn aus ih-ren Bett-lein auf,
daß sie oh-ne Sorg' und Mü-he fröh-lich sind im Ta-ges-lauf?

1. Gott der Herr hat sie ge-zäh-let, daß ihm auch nicht ei-nes feh-let an der
2. Gott der Herr rief sie mit Na-men, daß sie all ins Le-ben ka-men, daß sie
3. Gott im Him-mel hat an al-len sei-ne Lust und Wohl-ge-fal-len, kennt auch

gan-zen gro-ßen Zahl, an der gan-zen gro-ßen Zahl.
nun so fröh-lich sind, daß sie nun so fröh-lich sind.
dich und hat dich lieb, kennt auch dich und hat dich lieb.

1. Do you know how many stars
   Lighten up the evening sky?
   Do you know how many clouds
   Are there daily floating by?
   God the Lord keeps careful count,
   Every last one will be found,
   ||:May the number endless be.:||

2. Do you know how many insects
   Fly about each sunny day?
   Or how many little fish
   In the deep, cool waters play?
   God the Lord called each by name,
   Living creatures all became.
   ||: They are happy now and gay. :||

3. Do you know how many children
   Leap each morning from their beds?
   Start a day without a worry,
   Happy thoughts live in their heads.
   God the Lord cares for each girl and boy,
   His protection they all may enjoy,
   ||: Knows you well and loves you too. :||

Wiegenlied

Cradle Song

1. Gu - ten A - bend, gut'
2. Gu - ten A - bend, gut'

Nacht, mit Ro - sen be - dacht,___ mit Näg' - lein be -
Nacht, von Eng - lein be - wacht,___ die zei - gen im

steckt, schlupf' un - ter die Deck'. Mor - gen
Traum dir Christ - kind - leins Baum: Schlaf' nun

früh, wenn Gott will, wirst du wie - der ge - weckt, mor - gen
se - lig und süß, schau' im Traum 's Pa - ra - dies, schlaf' nun

früh, wenn Gott will, wirst du wie - der ge - weckt.
se - lig und süß, schau' im Traum 's Pa - ra - dies!

1. Lullaby and good night!
   With roses bedight,
   Creep into thy bed;
   There pillow thy head.
   If God will, thou shalt wake
   When the morning doth break,
   If God will, thou shalt wake
   When the morning doth break.

2. Lullaby and good night!
   Those blue eyes close tight,
   Bright angels are near,
   So sleep without fear.
   They will guard thee from harm
   With fair dreamland's sweet charm,
   They will guard thee from harm
   With fair dreamland's sweet charm.

Wollt ihr wissen, wie der Bauer

Do You Know Now How the Farmer

Vorsänger:
Alle:

A 1. Wollt ihr wis - sen, wie der Bau - er, wollt ihr wis - sen, wie der Bau - er sei - nen Ha - ber aus -

Vorsänger:
Alle:

B sät? Se - het so, so macht's der Bau - er, se - het so, so macht's der Bau - er, wenn er Ha - ber aus - sät.

2. Wollt ihr wissen, wie der Bauer
Wollt ihr wissen, wie der Bauer
Seinen Haber abmäht?
Sehet so, so macht's der Bauer,
Sehet so, so macht's der Bauer,
Wenn er Haber abmäht.

3. Wollt ihr wissen, wie der Bauer
Wollt ihr wissen, wie der Bauer
Seinen Haber einfährt?
Sehet so, so macht's der Bauer,
Sehet so, so macht's der Bauer,
Wenn er Haber einfährt.

4. Wollt ihr wissen, wie der Bauer
Wollt ihr wissen, wie der Bauer
Seinen Haber ausdrischt?
Sehet so, so macht's der Bauer,
Sehet so, so macht's der Bauer,
Wenn er Haber ausdrischt.

5. Wollt ihr wissen, wie der Bauer
Wollt ihr wissen, wie der Bauer
nach der Arbeit ausruht?
Sehet so, so macht's der Bauer,
Sehet so, so macht's der Bauer,
Wenn er abends ausruht.

6. Wollt ihr wissen, wie der Bauer
Wollt ihr wissen, wie der Bauer
Nach der Arbeit sich freut?
Sehet so, so machts der Bauer,
Sehet so, so machts der Bauer,
Wenn beim Tanz er sich dreht.

Spiellied aus dem Rheinland

Aufstellung: Die Kinder stehen im Kreis mit gefassten Händen; ein Kind in der Mitte.

Ausführung: A: Der Kreis geht nach links hin, der einzelne Bauer entgegengesetzt.

B: Der einzelne Bauer macht die Bewegungen vor, die Kinder im Kreis
machen sie nach. In Strophe 3 können jeweils 2 Kinder einen Wagen
darstellen. In der letzten Strophe holt sich der Bauer ein Kind aus
dem Kreis zum Tanzen, sie fassen sich an beiden Händen and hüpfen
so herum, gleichzeitig hüpft auch der grosse Kreis.

1. Do you know now how the farmer,
   Do you know now how the farmer,
   Is scattering the seed?
   Watch me now, so works the farmer,
   Watch me now, so works the farmer,
   When he's sowing the seed.

2. Do you know now how the farmer,
   Do you know now how the farmer,
   Is reaping the grain?
   Watch me now, so works the farmer,
   Watch me now, so works the farmer,
   When he's reaping the grain.

3. Do you know now how the farmer,
   Do you know now how the farmer,
   Is bringing in the grain?
   Watch me now, so works the farmer,
   Watch me now, so works the farmer,
   When he's bringing in the grain.

4. Do you know now how the farmer,
   Do you know now how the farmer,
   Is threshing the grain?
   Watch me now, so works the farmer,
   Watch me now, so works the farmer,
   When he's threshing the grain.

5. Do you know now how the farmer,
   Do you know now how the farmer,
   Is resting from his work?
   Watch me now, so rests the farmer,
   Watch me now, so rests the farmer,
   When he's resting from his work.

6. Do you know now how the farmer,
   Do you know now how the farmer,
   Is enjoying himself?
   Watch me now, so does the farmer,
   Watch me now, so does the farmer,
   When he dances and twirls.

How to play:

Children stand in a circle holding hands, one child is in the center (the farmer).
As the children sing, the circle moves to the left, "the farmer" in the opposite
direction. He/she shows what the farmer does and the others copy it. In the
last verse, "the farmer" takes a child from the circle and, holding hands, they
dance around. Everybody dances.

Frau: Mäuschen was schleppst du dort
             mir das Stück Zucker fort

Mauschen: Liebe Frau, ach vergib,
             habe vier Kinder lieb;
             waren so hungrig noch.
             Gute Frau, lass mir's doch!

Da lachte die Frau in ihrem Sinn und sagte: "Nun, Mäuschen,
so lauf nur hin! Ich wollte ja meinem Kinde so-eben auch etwas
für den Hunger geben." Das Mäuschen lief fort, O wie geschwind!
Die Frau ging frohlich zu ihrem Kind.

201

Wollt ihr wissen, wie's die kleinen Mädchen machen

Shall I Tell You

Wollt ihr wis-sen, wollt ihr wis-sen, wie's die klei-nen Mäd-chen ma-chen? Püppchen wie-gen, Püppchen wie-gen, al-les dreht sich her-um.

2. Wollt ihr wissen, wollt ihr wissen,
   Wie's die kleinen Knaben machen?
   Peitsche schlagen, Peitsche schlagen,
   Alles dreht sich herum.

3. Wollt ihr wissen, wollt ihr wissen,
   Wie's die jungen Damen machen?
   Schleier ziehen, Schleier ziehen,
   Alles dreht sich herum.

4. Wollt ihr wissen, wollt ihr wissen,
   Wie's die alten Damen machen?
   Kaffee trinken, Kaffee trinken,
   Alles dreht sich herum.

5. Wollt ihr wissen, wollt ihr wissen,
   Wie's die jungen Herren machen?
   Hut abnehmen, Hut abnehmen,
   Alles dreht sich herum.

6. Wollt ihr wissen, wollt ihr wissen,
   Wie's die alten Herren machen?
   Zeitung lesen, Zeitung lesen,
   Alles dreht sich herum.

SPIELREGEL. Die Kinder tun, was die Verse vorschreiben, bei alles dreht sich herum wird
dies ausgeführt und dabei in die Hände geklatscht.

1. Shall I tell you, shall I tell you
   What the little girls are doing?
   Little dolls they rock and cradle.
   Turn around in your place.

2. Shall I tell you, shall I tell you
   What the little boys are doing?
   Cracking whips and cracking whips, and
   Turn around in your place.

3. Shall I tell you, shall I tell you
   What the young ladies are doing?
   Pulling veils across their faces.
   Turn around in your place.

4. Shall I tell you, shall I tell you
   What the old ladies are doing?
   Drinking coffee, drinking coffee.
   Turn around in your place.

5. Shall I tell you, shall I tell you
   What the younger men are doing?
   Lift their hats to greet the ladies.
   Turn around in your place.

6. Shall I tell you, shall I tell you
   What the older men are doing?
   Read the paper, read the paper
   Turn around in your place.

HOW TO PLAY:

Children stand in a circle and act out what they are singing.
With the last line, they turn around and clap their hands.

Männer Chöre

Der Herr ist getreu

God Never Forgets

1. Es sin-ken wohl Berge und Tä-ler zu Staub, Der Herr ist ge-
2. Der Ju-gend hell schimmernde Hoffnungen schön, Der Herr ist ge-
3. Das Al-ter er-fah-ren, er-probet, bewährt, Der Herr ist ge-
4. Drum kommt, ihr Mühsel'gen, beladen, betrübt, Der Herr ist ge-

treu, Dem rast-lo-sen Fit-tig der Zeit wird zu Raub
treu, Wie gol-di-ge Träu-me des Schla-fes ver-gehn;
treu, Den Kelch schwerer Lei-den und Prü-fun-gen leert,
treu, Mit all eu-ren La-sten zu dem, der euch liebt:

Schön-heit der Er-de; Ruhm, Reichtum und Pracht, Sie ver-
Op-fer der kal-ten, ver-ach-ten-den Welt, Sie wie
Trö-stet den Ster-ben-den, klagt sei-nen Tod, Fällt
Hoff-nung er-stor-ben, aufs neu-e er-blüht, Und

schwin-den bald al-le im Dunkel der Nacht; Der Herr ist ge-treu.
Ster-ne erblassen am Himmelsgezelt; Der Herr ist ge-treu.
Selbst wie die Träne vom Augenlicht-rot; Der Herr ist ge-treu.
Freu-de und Lie-be im Herzen erglüht; Der Herr ist ge-treu.

1. The mountains and valleys may sink and decay,
   God never forgets,
   And time with its restless wings onward may flee,
   Measuring cycles on cycles to be,
   Till he dips his grey plume in eternity's sea,
   God never forgets.

2. And youth with its buoyant hope painting the sky,
   God never forgets,
   May furl its bright pinions all bleeding and torn,
   Crushed to the earth by a proud world's deep scorn.
   And die like a star at the rising of morn,
   God never forgets.

3. Old age with its silver hair revered with years,
   God never forgets,
   In the cold vale of sorrow may pillow its head,
   Pray for the dying and weep for the dead;
   It drops from life's stage like a tear that is shed,
   God never forgets.

4. Come then, ye that weep at the close of the day,
   God never forgets,
   Yes, come with your bonds, and your cross, and your tears,
   Come with your blighted hopes, cherished for years,
   Come banish forebodings and bury your fears,
   God never forgets.

Das liebe, alte Buch

The Dear Old Book

1. In des Herzens tiefstem Schrein lebt ein Bild mir hell und klar:
2. Und ich schau ein ander Bild, 's-ist die lie-be Mut-ter mein,
3. O das war mein Pa-ra-dies, da dies Wort zum ersten Mal
4. Wenn mein Pilgerlauf zu End' und ich steh' an Jordans Strand,

'Sist die al-te Bi-bel in des Va-ters hand; Und ich
In der hand die Bi-bel, — Thränen flossen drauf. A-ber
Zu dem Kind gesprochen auf der Mutter Schoss! Als aus
Wenn des Todes Flügel mich so leis um-weht, Oeff-ne

seh' im A-bend-schein um ihn her die Kin-der-schaar, Ue-berm
ob dem al-ten Buch leuchtets wie Verklärungsschein, Denn im
je-nem heilgen Buch mich umfloss der er-ste Strahl Je-ner
du, mein Bi-bel-buch, mir den Blick ins Va-ter-land, Wo mein

Ganzen weht ein Hauch vom Heimatland.
Got-tes-wort ging ihr der Himmel auf.
ew'-gen Got-tes-welt, so herrlich gross.
Geist dann deine Sprache ganz versteht!

Chor.

Teures Buch, Teures Buch,

Gottes Buch! Gottes Buch! In dir find' ich göttlich Leben, teures

Buch! teures Buch! Balsam, der die Wun-den stillt, Licht, das

ad lib.

mir das Herz erfüllt, Immer lieber wirst du mir, du teures Buch.

In the heart its deepest shrine,
Lives a picture bright and clear;
It is the Bible in the hands
   Of Father dear.
And seen in the evening glow
Surrounded him by children;
Over everything comes a breeze
   From the homeland!

Then I see another view
It's my dear mother;
In her hand the Bible with tears
   Falling on it.
But from the old book shines
A beam of light, and
In the Word of God the
   Heavens opened for her.

Oh, that was my paradise
When this word for the first time was spoken
To the child on the Mother's lap
When for the first time
From this holy book,
The rays of light surrounded me
The everlasting world of God
   So wonderfully great.

When my life's journey ends,
  And I stand on Jordan's shore;
When the wings of death softly
   Enfold me
Open thou my Bible so I may
Have a glimpse of Heaven.
Where my spirit will fully understand
  . Thy word!

Chorus:

Precious book, precious book, God's book!
In you I find God given life, you precious book.
Balsam heals the wounds so drear
Light that fills my heart from fear
Ever loving you the more
    You precious book!

Sing, bet und geh
   auf Gottes Wegen,
Verricht' das deine
   nur getreu,
Und trau des Himmels
   reichem Segen,
So wird er bei dir
   werden neu;
Denn welcher seine
   Zuversicht
Auf Gott setzt, den
   verläßt er nicht.

Georg Neumark,
1621—1681.

Der Herr ist mein Hirte

The Lord is My Shepherd

1. Der Herr ist mein Hir - te, er wei - det mich, Wo ich auch wan - dern
2. Der Herr ist mein Hir - te; ich darf Ihm trau'n In Freu - de, wie im
3. Der Herr ist mein Hir - te, ich za - ge nicht, Geht's auch durch Spott und

mag, Ver - lässt in kei - ner Trüb - sal mich, Und führt mich Tag für Tag.
Leid; Zu Ihm um Kraft und Hül - fe schau'n Ist mei - ne Se - lig - keit.
Hohn, Er füh - ret mich durch Nacht zum Licht Hin - auf zu sei - nem Thron.

CHOR. *Schneller.*

Er liebt mich so,
Er liebt mich so,
Wie bin ich froh!
Wie bin ich froh!

Mein Hir - te liebt mich in - nig - lich; so in - nig - lich;

Auf grü - ner Au' im Mor - gen - tau, Da führt mein Hir - te mich.

1. The Lord is my shepherd. He leadeth me.
   Where e'er my footsteps rove
   He guides me through life's stressful ways
   And leads me day by day.

Chorus

   He loves me so. What joys I know.
   My saviour loves me fervently
   Through pastures green and morning's dew.
   There leads my Saviour me.

2. The Lord is my Shepherd. I trust in Him.
   In sorrow and in joy
   From Him all strength and help receive
   For all eternity.

3. The Lord is my shepherd. I shall not fear.
   Though scorn and strife loom drear
   From gloom to light, He leads me on
   Up to His heavenly throne.

Der Reichtum der Liebe

The Riches of Love

1. Die Schätze der Welt sind nicht mein, Ich habe nicht Silber noch
2. Die Schätze der Er - de vergehn, Sie bleiben in Trümmern zu-
3. Was einstens ich nannte Ge - winn, Das achte für Schaden ich
4. Komm, ist dieser Reichtum nicht dein, Umsonst darfst du nehmen und

Gold; Doch wie kann ich je glücklicher sein, Als wenn Jesus, mein
rück; Doch mein Reichtum hat ewig Besteh'n Auch der Tod kann nicht
nun; Nur nach einem noch stehet mein Sinn: In dem Glück sei-ner
frei: Grei - fe tief in die Fülle hin-ein, Bis dein Hungern und

Chorus

Heiland, mir hold!
stö-ren mein Glück.
Lie-be zu ruhn.   O das Meer seiner Liebe so tief,   Der
Dürsten vor - bei.

gött - li - chen Lie - be in Je - su! Weit mehr als die Welt   An

Schä - tzen hält Ist der Reichtum der Liebe in Je - su.

---

1. The treasures of earth are not mine,
   I hold not its silver and gold:
   But a treasure far greater is mine;
   I have riches of value untold.

2. The treasures of earth must all fail,
   Its riches and honor decay,
   But the riches of love that are mine
   Even death cannot take them away.

3. Compared with the riches of love,
   The wealth of the world is but dross;
   I will seek but Christ Jesus to win,
   And for him I count all things but loss.

4. Come, take of the riches of Christ,
   Exhaustless and free is the store;
   Of its wonderful fullness receive,
   Till you hunger and thirst nevermore.

Chorus

Oh, the depths of the riches of love
The riches of love in Christ Jesus!
Far better than gold, or wealth untold,
Are the riches of love in Christ Jesus.

207

Fäden aus reinem Gold

Beautiful Threads of Gold

1. Langsam entrollt im Le-benslauf Sich ein Ge - we - be hold;
2. Lie-be reicht uns das Weberschiff, Reicht uns die Fäden hold,
3. Ob treu das Herz, der Meister sieht's, Rechnet danach den Sold,
4. Ei - lend entrinnt der Arbeitstag. Was wir zu tun ge-wollt,

Lieblich durchstrahlen hier und dort Fäden aus rei - nem Gold.
Dass in dem Werk enzückt wir sehn Fäden aus rei - nem Gold.
Sucht in des Webers Ar-beit nur Fäden aus rei - nem Gold.
Zeigt manchen Fehler, doch da - bei Fäden aus rei - nem Gold.

Schimmerndes Licht wie Sonnenschein Strahlet dem Weber Freude ein;
Weben wir fleissig al - le - zeit, Fröhlich und treu in Freud' und Leid,
Hilft froh-bereit der schwachen Hand, Die sonst das Weben schwierig fand,
Liebe, die uns das Werk gelehrt, Zaubrisch durchwebt, was schlecht verkehrt.

Leuchtend vergeltend Streben rein Fäden aus rei-nem Gold.
Leuchten für uns in E-wig - keit· Fäden aus rei-nem Gold.
Webt für sie in das Le-bens-band Fäden aus rei-nem Gold.
Mit je - ner Pracht, die neu verklärt, Fäden aus rei-nem Gold.

1. Slowly the web of life unrolls, Shimmering fold on fold,
Somber and bright and ashen gray, Woven with threads of gold.
Glittering threads like sunshine fair, Lighting the woof of toil and care,
Making the web a fabric rare, Beautiful threads of gold.

2. Gather we now the gleaming strands, All that our hands will hold,
Tossing the shuttle to and fro, Weaving our threads of gold.
Weaving them in thro' smiles and tears, Weaving them in thro' hopes and fears,
Weaving them in thro' passing years, Beautiful threads of gold.

3. Over us still the Master's eye Watches the web unfold,
Sees in the loom his pattern grow, Rich with its threads of gold.
Patient the Master Weaver stands, Guides with his own our childish hands,
Holding the fair and shining strands, Beautiful threads of gold.

4. Swiftly the years may come and go, Faded the web and old,
Yet will their luster brighter grow, Beautiful threads of gold.
Under the good the threads will run, Over the wrong that we have done,
Wonderful threads that love has spun, Beautiful threads of gold.

Mein Anker hält

My Anchor Holds

1. Ob die Brandung tobt und grollt, Blitze zucken, Donner rollt,
2. Um mich braust der Spötter Hohn, Die mich zu verschlingen drohn:
3. Lass die Wetter mich umziehn, Heisser Kämpfe Feuer glühn:

Ob auch braust der Wogen Heer. Fürchte ich mich nimmermehr:
Steigt der Bos - heit Flu-ten hoch Ueber mich, so weiss ich doch,
Du, in dem mein Glaube ruht, Bringe mich durch Sturm und Flut,

Ja, ob un - ter-ging' die Welt, Denn ich weiss, mein Anker hält.
Dass sie an dem Fels zerschellt, Welcher mei - nen Anker hält.
Wie es, Hei-land dir gefällt, Denn ich weiss, mein Anker hält.

Chorus

Ja, er hält, mein Anker hält, Ob auch Wo-gen wild und

er hält

schwer Toben um mein Schifflein her: Ihr versenkt es nimmer-

und schwer

mer, Denn mein An - ker hält, mein An - ker hält.

ich weiss er hält

1. **Though the angry surges roll** On my tempest driven soul,
I am peaceful, for I know, Wildly tho' the winds may blow,
I've an anchor safe and sure, That shall evermore endure.

Chorus

And it holds, my anchor holds; Blow your wildest, then, O gale,
On my bark so small and frail; I shall never, never fail,
For my anchor holds, my anchor holds.

2. Mighty tides about me sweep; Perils lurk within the deep;
Angry clouds o'ershade the sky, And the tempest rises high;
Still I stand the tempest's shock, For my anchor grips the rock.

3. Troubles almost 'whelm the soul, Griefs like billows o'er me roll;
Tempters seek to lure astray, Storms obscure the light of day;
I can face them and be bold, — I've an anchor that shall hold.

Ruh', Soldat, nun aus

Soldier, Rest in Peace

1. Ruh', Soldat, nun aus, überwunden hast du; Nach schwerem Kampf ward dir
2. Traum nicht mehr von Schlachten Vorbei ist der Krieg; Norden und Süden dankt

endlich die Ruh'! Mil-li-o-nen beuget, was schwer dich einst traf;
heut für den Sieg. Ster-nen-banner einet, die tüchtig und brav,

Sieh', wir ge-den-ken dein, schla-fe nur, schlaf.
Sieh', wir ge-den-ken dein, schla-fe nur, schlaf. Schla - fe!

doch un-ver-ges - sen Ist, was du ta - test in Kampf und Müh'.

Schlummre! das Volk der Frei-en Ver-gis-set euch Hel - den nie!

1. Soldier, rest in peace! now is over thy strife;
   Well hast thou won in the battle of life!
   O'er thy grave the millions their kind vigil keep;
   Thou art remembered yet, peacefully sleep.

2. Dream no more of battle, the vict'ry is won,
   Hearts disunited are beating as one;
   Freedom rules the nation, our colors wide sweep;
   Thou art remembered yet, peacefully sleep.

Chorus

Sleeping! yet not forgotten,
Thy toils and griefs are remembered yet;
Slumber, assured the nation
Her heroes ne'er will forget!

210

Vŏrwarts, mit dem Kreuzpanier

Forward, Soldiers of the Cross

1. Vorwärts, vorwärts, heil'ge Streiter ihr, Vorwärts, vorwärts,
2. Ei - let, ei - let, ist auch rauh der Weg, Je-su Hee - re
3. Mu - tig, mu - tig, auf der Streiter Bahn, Furchtlos, furchtlos,
4. Rastlos, rast - los, bis der Kampf vorbei; Streiter Je - su,

mit dem Kreuzpanier! Hebt das Lie-bes-ban-ner hoch em - por
brechen durch's Geheg'; Vorwärts vorwärts ist der Tag auch schwühl,
Je - sus geht voran; Er hilft kämpfen, hilft in je - der Not,
kämpft im Glauben treu; Triumph, Triumph, klingt's dann laut und hehr,

Chorus

Vorwärts, vorwärts, dringet siegreich vor.
Kro-nen winken nach dem Kampfgewühl.
Und be - sie - get Sünde, Höll' und Tod.
Hal - le - lu - ja, Gott sei Lob und Ehr'.

Horcht, wie siegreich klingt das

Losungswort: Vorwärts, vorwärts, seht die Fahne dort! Christus führt euch

in den heil'gen Krieg, Vorwärts, Streiter, herrlich ist der Sieg.

1. Forward, forward, soldiers of the cross!
   Forward, forward! counting all but loss,
   Love's fair banner lift against the sky;
   Forward, forward, victory is nigh.

2. Marching! marching o'er the toilsome way,
   Jesus' legions may not now delay;
   Forward! forward thro' the battle's din,
   Crowns unfading in his name to win.

   Chorus

3. Courage! courage, loyal hearts and true;
   Fear not, fear not, Jesus fights for you;
   Trust him trust him praise his holy name,
   He has conquered sin and death and shame.

4. Rest not, rest not, till the day is done!
   Life's long battle will at last be won;
   Shouts of triumph thro' his courts will ring,
   Alleluia unto Christ the King!

Hark! this watchword rings along the line,
Follow, follow where the colors shine!
Christ your Captain gives the rallying call,
Loyal soldiers, forward, forward all!

Wie wohl ist mir

How Well I Feel

1. Wie wohl ist mir, wie froh bin ich Wenn sich mein Glaube, Herr, in dich
2. So oft mein Herz da-ran gedenkt, Gott ha - be mir den Sohn geschenkt,
3. So werd ich vol - ler Zu-ver-sicht Und komme vor dein An-ge-sicht,

In dein Verdienst versenkt und spricht, Ich lasse meinen Je-sum nicht.
Es komme sein Versöhnungsblut Auch mir unnützem Knecht zu gut.
Im Glauben dir mein Herz zu weihn, Und weiss, du werdest gnädig sein.

Chorus

Wie wohl ist mir, wie froh bin ich,
Wie wohl ist mir, wie froh bin ich, Mein

Herz tief in Gott versenket sich. Wie wohl ist mir
Herz in Gott versenket sich Wie wohl ist mir

in meinem Geist.
in meinem Geist Er - ful-let Gott was er verheisst.

1. How well I feel, how glad am I
   That all my faith is Lord in Thee
   Deep on your grace I will rely
   Your loyal servant here to be.

2. So often as my heart recalls
   How God to me His Son did give;
   His cleansing spirit now fulfills
   The promise that my Saviour lives.

3. So will I ever trusting be
   That I Thy loving face shall see
   In faith my heart to you I'll give
   For in your presence I shall live.

Chorus

How well I feel, now glad am I
My heart on God it will rely
How well I feel within my soul
Forever God is in control.

212

Alphabetical Index

CONTENTS	PAGE

CONTENTS	PAGE

CONTENTS   PAGE   CONTENTS   PAGE